Stanley Thornes (Publishers) Ltd

Do you receive **BLUEPRINTS NEWS**?

Blueprints is an expanding series of practical teacher's ideas books and photocopiable resources for use in primary schools. Books are available for separate infant and junior age ranges for every core and foundation subject, as well as for an ever widening range of other primary teaching needs. These include **Blueprints Primary English** books and **Blueprints Resource Banks**. **Blueprints** are carefully structured around the demands of the National Curriculum in England and Wales, but are used successfully by schools and teachers in Scotland, Northern Ireland and elsewhere.

Blueprints provide:
- *Total curriculum coverage*
- *Hundreds of practical ideas*
- *Books specifically for the age range you teach*
- *Flexible resources for the whole school or for individual teachers*
- *Excellent photocopiable sheets – ideal for assessment and children's work profiles*
- *Supreme value.*

Books may be bought by credit card over the telephone and information obtained on **(01242) 577944**. Alternatively, photocopy and return this **FREEPOST** form to receive **Blueprints News**, our regular update on all new and existing titles. You may also like to add the name of a friend who would be interested in being on the mailing list.

Please add my name to the **BLUEPRINTS NEWS** mailing list.

Mr/Mrs/Miss/Ms _____

Home address _____

_____ Postcode _____

School address _____

_____ Postcode _____

Please also send **BLUEPRINTS NEWS** to:

Mr/Mrs/Miss/Ms _____

Address _____

_____ Postcode _____

To: Marketing Services Dept., Stanley Thornes Ltd, FREEPOST (GR 782), Cheltenham, GL50 1BR

Text © Ron Adams 1997

Original line illustrations © ST(P) Ltd 1997

The right of Ron Adams to be identified as author of this work has been asserted by him in accordance with the Copyright, Designs and Patents Act 1988.

Acknowledgements: The author wishes to thank Julia Hawkins, Science Co-ordinator at Walwayne Court School, Trowbridge, and Geoff Cresswell, Schools Science Inspector, for their help in the preparation of this book.

First published in 1997 by:
Stanley Thornes (Publishers) Ltd
Ellenborough House
Wellington Street
CHELTENHAM GL50 1YW

A catalogue record for this book is available from the British Library.

ISBN 0–7487–3446–5

Typeset by John Youé Books Design
Printed and bound in Great Britain

97 98 99 00 01 / 10 9 8 7 6 5 4 3 2

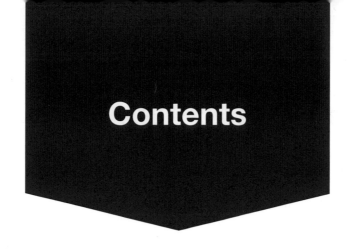

Contents

Introduction	iv
How to use this book	v
AT1: Experimental and Investigative Science	1

Level 1
1 Describe features of living things — 1
2 Describe simple features of objects — 1
3 Describe simple features of animals — 1

Level 2
4 Respond to suggestions, predict — 2
5 Respond to and make suggestions — 2
6 Make suggestions, draw conclusions — 3
7 Compare living things — 3
8 Compare events — 3
9 Compare objects — 4
10 Make predictions, record observations — 4

Level 3
11 Record observations, make predictions — 4
12 Fair test with help — 5

AT2: Life Processes and Living Things — 6

Level 1
1 Recognize and name parts of the body — 6
2 Recognize and name parts of plant — 6
3 Observe, describe animals and plants — 6
4 Recognize and name animals — 7

Level 2
5 Describe basic plant conditions — 7
6 Reproduction — 7
7 Group using simple features — 8
8 Sort according to observable features — 8
9 Living things in different places — 8

Level 3
10 Living and non-living things — 9
11 Diet affects the health of humans — 9
12 Diet affects teeth — 9
13 Exercise affects the health of humans — 10
14 The effect of water and light on plants — 10
15 Exploring habitats — 10

AT 3: Materials and their Properties — 11

Level 1
1 Describe materials — 11
2 Describe materials by their properties — 11

Level 2
3 Identify materials by their properties — 12
4 Describe similarities and differences — 12
5 Sorting materials — 12
6 Changes in materials — 13

Level 3
7 Sorting materials by their properties — 13
8 Suitable materials — 13
9 Reversible/irreversible changes — 14
10 Natural and made materials — 14
11 Mass and size of materials — 14

AT4: Physical Processes — 15

Level 1
1 Describe changes in light — 15
2 Describe changes in sound — 15
3 Pushing and pulling objects — 15
4 Identify and name light sources — 16
5 Identify and name sound sources — 16

Level 2
6 How bulbs work — 16
7 Sounds — 16
8 Compare movement – direction/speed — 17

Level 3
9 Light fails because of break in circuit — 17
10 Applied forces affect direction/speed — 17
11 Sideways pushes/pulls cause swerves — 18
12 Pulls/pushes can change some shapes — 18
13 Sounds become louder — 18

Copymasters 1-102

Record Sheet 1 Class Record

Record Sheet 2 Child's Record

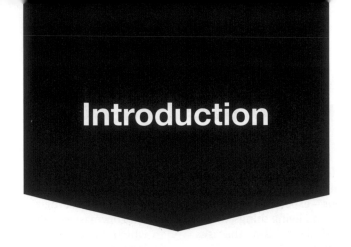

Introduction

An important part of a teacher's work is the constant assessment of children's learning. Only by assessing can we decide what children should do next and give them tasks that are appropriate. It is to support teachers in their assessment of children's work in science that this book has been written. The assessment tasks are intended to support teachers in forming their own assessments of what children know and can do. The exercises are not intended as rigorous in-depth 'tests'. Rather, they are indicators or clues to where the children have reached, and they are intended to have a predominantly formative purpose. The tasks employ a range of learning modes; many employ practical work and experimentation, others are more paper-based, but overall we have tried to provide opportunities for hands-on work either to introduce or to follow-up the task even where the assessment itself only uses information on the copymaster. All the activities have been tried and tested in schools to ensure that they work; many have been modified and adapted in the light of classroom testing.

USING BLUEPRINTS SCIENCE ASSESSMENT
Blueprints Science Assessment is a practical teacher's resource specifically tied in to the requirements of the National Curriculum for science in primary schools. It offers assessment tasks which teachers can use alongside those they devise themselves, or with more formal 'tests'. *Blueprints Science Assessment: Key Stage 1* provides tasks for children between 5 and 7 years old; *Blueprints Science Assessment: Key stage 2* provides tasks for children between 7 and 11 years old. Teacher's notes and assessment copymasters are combined in one book for each Key Stage. The sequence the exercises follow matches that of the content of *Science in the National Curriculum (1995).*

Blueprints Science Assessment: Key Stage 1 provides a set of assessment tasks through Key Stage 1. The assessment exercises are arranged in four sections, each related to the assessment of work expected of children through this Key Stage: Attainment Targets 1, 2, 3, and 4 at Levels 1–3. Although there are frequent opportunities to observe children's grasp of AT1 (Experimental and Investigative Science) whilst working on assessments for the other Attainment Targets, we have provided a bank of assessment purely focused on this AT and using contexts drawn from the other areas of science.

At the start of the teacher's notes about the assessment tasks relating to each Level of each Attainment Target there is an extract from the Statutory Orders, comprising the Attainment Target title, and the appropriate Level Description. For each assessment task there are two copymasters. The first of these is labelled 'A'. This is the key assessment sheet for that part of the curriculum. For all tasks there are also reassessment copymasters, labelled 'B'. Each of these appears immediately after each ' first try' copymaster, and closely follows the content of the A sheet with different examples. The reassessment sheets can be used in a number of different ways:

- for children to do as an addition to the first assessment task
- where children make mistakes on the first task, as a second try at a later date
- where a group of children are doing the task at the same time some can be given the A sheet and others the B sheet

The tasks call for varying amounts of preparation and resources but all provide opportunities to develop practical work if required and can be embedded into your ongoing science work as part of a lively and practical programme. The organization of the tasks is usually for each child to work individually, although some do require paired work to keep the resources required to a feasible level. You will find that each task has a key question which will enable you to focus on the core behaviour or skill which the child needs to demonstrate. The sheets usually involve direct pupil completion, but some, particularly at the lower levels, require teacher observation and written comment.

RECORD KEEPING
There are two summary record sheets at the back of the book. The first is a tick list to enable you to record which children in the class have done each task at a specific Level. The second is a tick list that can be kept for each child, showing those tasks the child has tried and which of them the child has completed successfully. Photocopy one Record Sheet 1 per class to maintain a tick list to show assessment tasks tried at a specific Level. Photocopy one Record Sheet 2 per child and tick the assessment tasks tried, those done successfully and reassessment attempts where appropriate. This record sheet can be added to school records.

How to use this book

This book has been tied to National Curriculum Attainment Targets so that the assessment tasks can be accessed easily. Within each of the sections – experimental and investigative science, life processes and living things, materials and their properties, and physical processes – the tasks have been arranged by Level, with Level 1 exercises first, and so on. The intention has been to provide a bank of short assessment tasks covering all Attainment Targets. However, I hope that readers will, rather than taking the book wholesale, choose and use those tasks which they find most useful, to support their own assessment judgements.

The copymasters (labelled 'A') are also marked to indicate to which AT and Level they refer. Reassessment copymasters are labelled 'B'. At the end of the book are two record sheets, enabling you to keep a class record and a record of the assessment tasks tried by each child.

AT1: Experimental and Investigative Science

LEVEL 1

Level Description

Pupils describe simple features of objects, living things and events they observe, communicating their findings in simple ways, such as talking about their work or through drawings or simple charts.

TASK 1 — DESCRIBE FEATURES OF LIVING THINGS A/B
C1-2

Resources
A variety of fruits cut in half including, if possible, an apple and an orange, and reference books, copymaster C1, magnifying glasses.

Organization
This can be done individually or in small groups.

What you do
Ask the children what colour the fruits are and what shape they are. Ask them to find the number and position of seeds, the size of the seeds, to describe the taste and the smell of the fruits. Encourage discussion through investigation and note descriptive language on the bottom of the copymaster. Give out copies of the copymaster and explain the task which is to draw a chosen piece of fruit and its seed (using a magnifying glass); to colour outlines of the fruits shown using realistic colours (pastels produce some very good results for this); to tell you how the fruits are different. For the colouring, which should be based upon observation, supply either an apple and an orange cut in two, or pictures of them.

What the child does
The child observes the fruits in detail and discusses them, as above; compares the differences between the fruits; chooses one and draws it in some detail including its seed; observes and colours an apple and an orange.

Key question
Can the child describe simple features of things with words and pictures?

Reassessment
Use copymaster C2, reference books, a variety of vegetables (some cut in half or cut open) for reassessment. The task on C2 is the same as that on C1 but using vegetables instead of fruit. Include an onion and a carrot.

TASK 2 — DESCRIBE SIMPLE FEATURES OF OBJECTS A/B
C3-4

Resources
Magnets, spoons, rubbers, keys, 10p coins, rulers, pencils and aluminium cans, copymaster C3.

Organization
This is an individual task.

What you do
Give out copies of the copymaster and explain the task which is to test which objects are attracted by magnets and, on the copymaster, to colour red those objects picked up by a magnet and to colour green those that are not. Encourage discussion throughout the investigation.

What the child does
The child tests to see which objects a magnet will pick up and discusses the results (findings) with other children and the teacher. The child records the results by colouring the appropriate objects.

Key question
Can the child describe simple events that they observe?

Reassessment
Use copymaster C4 and the following resources for the same investigation: plastic spoon, jumbo-sized paper clip, 2p coins, felt-tip pens, 50p coins, pieces of aluminium foil, large washers.

TASK 3 — DESCRIBE SIMPLE FEATURES OF ANIMALS A/B
C5-6

Resources
Copymaster C5, books, coloured pencils (crayons are not suitable for this task).

Organization
This is an individual task.

What you do
Give out copies of the copymaster and explain the task which is to colour the outlines of drawings in a realistic way and to describe through talk the simple features of the animals. Ask the children questions about the animals. What colour are they? Have they got fur coats? Do they have long tails? How many legs have they got? Record examples of their descriptive language on the copymaster.

What the child does
The child completes the task on the copymaster and talks about the animals.

Key question
Can the child describe simple features of animals?

Reassessment
Use reference books and copymaster C6. The task is as before, but involving different animals.

LEVEL 2

Level 2 Level Description

Pupils respond to suggestions of how to find things out and, with help, make their own suggestions. They use simple equipment provided and make observations related to their task. They compare objects, living things and events they observe. They describe their observations and record them using simple tables where it is appropriate to do so. They say whether what has happened was what they expected.

TASK 4
C7-8

RESPOND TO SUGGESTIONS, PREDICT A/B

Resources
Copymaster C7, torches, bricks, coloured bottles, thick card, tracing paper, pieces of black polythene.

Organization
This is an individual task.

What you do
Encourage the children to predict which objects allow light to pass through and why they think so. Encourage them to suggest how to test the objects. Give out copymaster C7 and explain the task which is to say whether they expect to be able to see through the materials (clearly, a bit or not at all) then to use a torch and test the materials and record the results. Ask questions during the investigation, eg 'why do you think the black plastic did not stop all of the light?'.

What the child does
The child predicts and then tests to find out which materials are opaque, translucent or transparent; records predictions and results.

Key question
Can the child make their own predictions and respond to suggestions of how to find things out?

Reassessment
Retest using copymaster C8 and the following resources: wood, coloured water, leaves, curtains, clean water and torches.

TASK 5
C9-10

RESPOND TO AND MAKE SUGGESTIONS A/B

Resources
Copymaster C9, toy cars with freely moving wheels, metre-long (approximately) strips of rigid smooth materials (eg plywood) a number of thick books, a long table.

Organization
This task can be done in pairs.

What you do
Give out copymaster C9 and explain the task which is to suggest which of the illustrated cars will travel the furthest; to measure the distance travelled in each case and to say whether what happened is what they expected. Encourage the children to predict which car will travel furthest along the table surface after rolling down the slope. Encourage the children to suggest how to test the four different slopes and how they can make accurate measurements, eg start at the same point on the slope each time, position the books at the same support point, measure along the table from the same point each time.

What the child does
The children respond to suggestions, make their own and then test and record the results. They describe what happened and say whether it was what they expected.

Key question
Can each child make their own predictions and respond to suggestions of how to find things out?

Reassessment
Use copymaster C10. The task is the same but uses a soft ball instead of a toy car.

TASK 6 C11-12

MAKE SUGGESTIONS, DRAW CONCLUSIONS A/B

Resources
Copymaster C11, brown sugar, salt, sand, containers (in threes), teaspoons, stirrers, warm water, timers.

Organization
This task can be done individually or in pairs but monitor individual input.

What you do
Give out copymaster C11 and explain that the task is to suggest which substances will dissolve in warm water and to observe how long it takes for them to dissolve. Encourage the children to suggest which substances will dissolve in the water and to say why they think so. Encourage the children to suggest how to organize the test, eg to stir each mixture for a set time. Ask questions during the investigation, eg 'why do you think the sand is not dissolving?'.

What the child does
Each child makes suggestions, conducts the investigation and draws conclusions.

Key question
Can the child draw a conclusion (eg that one of the materials dissolves faster from the others)?

Reassessment
Use copymaster C12 and the following resources: rice, jelly cubes, white sugar, cold water.

TASK 7 C13-14

COMPARE LIVING THINGS A/B

Resources
Copymaster C13, small land animals, plastic containers, hand lenses or magnifiers, rulers, coloured pencils.

Organization
This task can be done individually or in pairs.

What you do
Give out copies of copymaster C13 and explain the task which is to choose two small land animals and to name them; to make drawings of both animals and then to test the differences and similarities between them. Allow the children to collect a range of animals and leave enough time for them to study the animals. Emphasize the need to take care of the creatures. Encourage the use of magnifiers and suggest that they look at two creatures in detail (not necessarily from the same classification group, eg a slug and centipede). Encourage the children to draw large detailed pictures of the animals and to record the similarities and differences, not only their appearance but also movement. Encourage them to use a ruler to give scale to the drawings.

What the child does
Each child collects land animals, selects two for close examination, draws them and annotates the drawings, and compares the two, identifying similarities and differences. If the child cannot write down the similarities and differences, act as scribe.

Key question
Can the child use simple equipment (eg magnifiers, rulers) and make careful observations? Can the child compare the living things that he has observed?

Reassessment
Use copymaster C14. Repeat the task described above but using different small land animals, or pond animals (if you have access to a pond) such as a shrimp and a nymph.

TASK 8 C15-16

COMPARE EVENTS A/B

Resources
Copymaster C15, salt, fine gravel, talcum powder, plaster of Paris, potting compost, sugar, plastic containers, stirrers, water.

Organization
This task can be done individually or in pairs but monitor individual input.

What you do
Give out copies of copymaster C15 and explain the task which is to try to dissolve materials in water by stirring; to record what happens and to compare events and draw a conclusion. Suggest that the children spend the same amount of time stirring each mixture. Encourage the children to record their observations using the copymaster classifications and their own notes.

What the child does
Each child completes the tasks on the copymaster, compares the samples in terms of those that dissolved, floated, sank or changed in some other way (the plaster solidifies), uses simple tables to record the results, and uses equipment in a consistent way.

Key question
Can the child compare events that they observe, using a simple table to record results? Can the child use equipment and make measurements consistently?

Reassessment
Repeat the task using copymaster C16 and the following substances: bath crystals, wood chippings, baking powder, flour, sand, coffee powder.

TASK 9 — C17-18: COMPARE OBJECTS A/B

Resources
Copymaster C17, a variety of objects with clearly different characteristics including transparent flexible rulers, safety mirrors, wood, Plasticine®, iron nails, feathers, bricks, aluminium cans.

Organization
The child works individually.

What you do
Allow children to investigate the resources and compare their properties. Give out copies of copymaster C17 and explain the task which is to join the objects to words that describe them (objects can be joined to more than one word). Allow the children to link the objects with all the words that could describe them, eg the flexible ruler would link with the words flexible and transparent, the nail with hard, rigid, shiny (when new).

What the child does
Each child examines resources and compares their properties and completes the tasks on the copymaster.

Key question
Can the child compare objects they observe?

Reassessment
Repeat the task on copymaster C18 which requires a metal safety ruler, clay, a copper coin, a stone, glass, cotton wool, a mug, a balloon, a sponge.

TASK 10 — C19-20: MAKE PREDICTIONS, RECORD OBSERVATIONS A/B

Resources
Copymaster C19, golf, tennis, table tennis and cricket balls, metre-long rulers.

Organization
The children work in pairs but monitor individual input.

What you do
Give out copies of copymaster C19 and explain the task which is to predict which ball will bounce the highest when dropped from 1 metre high and which ball will bounce the lowest when dropped from the same height; to record the highest and lowest bounces and to explain whether the results were as expected or not.

What the child does
Each child predicts, carries out the investigation, records observations and draws conclusions.

Key question
Can the child put forward ideas and make simple predictions? Can the child make observations and measure length using simple equipment?

Reassessment
Use copymaster C20. Repeat the task but using some different balls: squash balls, rubber balls, golf balls and sponge rubber balls.

LEVEL 3 — Level 3 Level Description

Pupils respond to suggestions, put forward their own ideas and, where appropriate, make simple predictions. They make relevant observations and measure quantities, such as length or mass, using a range of simple equipment. With some help they carry out a fair test, recognising and explaining why it is fair. They record their observations in a variety of ways. They provide explanations for observations and, where they occur, for simple patterns in recorded measurements. They say what they have found out from their work.

TASK 11 — C21-22: RECORD OBSERVATIONS, MAKE PREDICTIONS A/B

Resources
Copymaster C21, wool, plastic, paper, warm water.

Organization
The children work in pairs but monitor individual input.

What you do
Give out copies of copymaster C21 and explain the task which is to find out which of the given materials provides the best heat insulation; to draw a bar graph to show how the temperature varies for each material after 20 minutes. Help the children ensure fair testing by keeping variables unchanged (such as using the same amount of material for wrapping round a beaker of warm water). Ensure tests are concurrent to reduce the length of time needed for experiment. Start with water at 50°C.

What the child does
The child thinks about and responds to questions, makes suggestions about how to investigate which clothes are the warmest (could use drawings to explain their ideas) and completes the tasks on the copymaster and records the temperature of water at 5-minute intervals, using the

information to produce a bar chart and to draw conclusions.

Key question
Can the child make simple predictions based on everyday experience which can be tested? Can the child record observations using a bar chart?

Reassessment
Use copymaster C22 and the following materials: polythene, wool and nylon to test which material will provide the best waterproofing.

TASK 12 — FAIR TEST WITH HELP A/B

C23 -24

Resources
Copymaster C23.

Organization
Each child works individually.

What you do
Discuss the need to conduct fair tests and how to ensure fairness, eg by just changing one factor at a time. Give out copies of the copymaster and explain the task which is to identify the conditions of a fair test of an investigation into the stretching of various threads, strings and ropes.

What the child does
The child studies the copymaster and completes the task.

Key question
Does the child understand how a fair test could be carried out?

Reassessment
Use copymaster C24.

AT2: Life Processes and Living Things

Level Description

Pupils recognise and name external parts of the body, using words such as head or arm, and of plants, using words such as leaf or flower. They observe and describe a range of animals and plants in terms of features such as colour of coat, or size of leaf. They recognise and identify a range of common animals, using terms such as fly, goldfish or robin.

TASK 1 — C25-26 — RECOGNIZE AND NAME PARTS OF THE BODY A/B

Resources
Copymaster C25.

Organization
Each child works individually.

What you do
Give out copies of copymaster C25 and explain the task which is to recognize parts of the human body and link the labels to the correct parts using arrows.

What the child does
The child draws arrows to identify the correct parts of the human body.

Key question
Can the child recognize and name the external parts of the human body?

Reassessment
Use copymaster C26 to test the child on recognition of parts of the face.

TASK 2 — C27-28 — RECOGNIZE AND NAME PARTS OF PLANTS A/B

Resources
Copymaster C27.

Organization
Each child works individually.

What you do
Give out copies of copymaster C27 and explain the task which is to draw arrows to connect the parts of the plant to their names.

What the child does
The child completes the tasks in the copymaster.

Key question
Can the child identify and name the external parts of a plant?

Reassessment
Use copymaster C28. The task is to colour the parts of the plant.

TASK 3 — C29-30 — OBSERVE, DESCRIBE ANIMALS AND PLANTS A/B

Resources
Copymasters C29, photographs of animals.

Organization
Each child works individually.

What you do
Give children colour photographs of animals including those illustrated on the copymaster to look at and discuss. Give out copies of copymaster C29 and explain the task which is to study the illustrations and to use coloured pencils to colour them realistically, then to say which animals are always the same colour.

What the child does
The child studies the copymaster, colours in the animals appropriately, then names and identifies which animals are always the same colour.

Key question

Can the child observe and describe a range of animals?

Reassessment

Use copymaster C30. Children observe and describe which plants have large leaves and which have small leaves.

TASK 4
C31-32

RECOGNIZE AND NAME ANIMALS A/B

Resources

Copymaster C31.

Organization

Each child works individually.

What you do

Provide colour illustrations of the animals shown on the copymaster. Give out copymaster C31 and explain the task which is to recognize the animals and name them by using arrows to link the animals with their names. Where necessary, help the children with reading the copymaster.

What the child does

The child draws an arrow from each animal to its correct name.

Key question

Can the child identify a range of common animals?

Reassessment

Use copymaster C32 which includes different animals. As an extra activity, get the children to collect minibeasts and to draw them in picture frames, then to identify and name them underneath their drawings from information found in picture books.

LEVEL 2

Level Description

Pupils use their knowledge about living things to describe basic conditions, such as a supply of food, water, air or light, that animals and plants need in order to survive. They recognise that living things grow and reproduce. They sort living things into groups, using simple features. They describe the basis for their groupings in terms such as number of legs or shape of leaf. They recognise that different living things are found in different places, such as ponds or woods.

TASK 5
C33-34

DESCRIBE BASIC PLANT CONDITIONS A/B

Resources

Two pots with cress plants per child, water, jug and copymaster C33.

Organization

Each child works individually.

What you do

Ask the children to predict what they think will happen when one plant is watered whilst the other is not. Other questions that you could ask include the following. How much water shall we give the plant? What will happen if we over-water one plant? How shall we measure how much the plants grow? Give the children copies of copymaster C33 to complete the task. Help the children to do the investigation and describe what happens and why.

What the child does

With help, the child sets up a simple experiment with two plants (this will involve the initial growing of the cress), waters one regularly and stops watering the other completely, then observes the two plants over a period of time after predicting what will happen. The child records what happens to the two plants, explains why and completes the tasks in the copymaster.

Key question

Does the child understand that most plants need water to survive and remain healthy?

Reassessment

Use copymaster C34. This is a similar experiment but concerning a plant's need for light; put a pot of cress in a dark cupboard, leave the other on a window sill. Children observe and describe the importance of light for plants.

TASK 6
C35-36

REPRODUCTION A/B

Resources

Copymaster C35, reference picture books on animals.

Organization

Each child works individually.

What you do

Give out copies of the copymaster and explain the task which is to draw a line between the adult animals and the young they produce.

What the child does

The child completes the task.

Key question
Does the child know that living things grow and reproduce?

Reassessment
Use copymaster C36 which has the same task but with different animals.

TASK 7 C37-38

GROUP USING SIMPLE FEATURES A/B

Resources
Copymaster C37.

Organization
The children can work individually or in pairs but monitor individual input.

What you do
Give out copymaster C37 and explain the task which is to count the number of boys and girls in the class who have blond, black, brown hair and use this data to make a block graph. Encourage the children to count accurately and to draw their graphs with precision.

What the child does
The child counts how many boys and girls in the class have the various hair colours and draws a graph to record the results accurately.

Key question
Can the child sort living things into groups using simple features?

Reassessment
Use copymaster C38. The task here is to count and sort the children according to eye colour.

TASK 8 C39-40

SORT ACCORDING TO OBSERVABLE FEATURES A/B

Resources
Copymaster C39 and reference books.

Organization
Each child works individually.

What you do
Give out copymaster C39 and explain the task which is to look at the illustrations and to draw a red circle round those creatures with six legs, a blue circle round those with eight legs and a yellow circle round those with more than eight legs.

What the child does
The child completes the task on the copymaster.

Key question
Can the child sort living things into groups using observable features?

Reassessment
Use copymaster C40 to sort leaves out into three groups: large, small and long thin ones.

TASK 9 C41-42

LIVING THINGS IN DIFFERENT PLACES A/B

Resources
Copymaster C41, note pads, pencils, reference books for plant and animal identification.

Organization
The children can work individually or in pairs but monitor individual input.

What you do
Give out copies of copymaster C41 and set the task for the children which is to study three different local habitats (such as a pond, a school field and a wooded area); to make a record on the copymaster of the amount of water, shade, plant life, and large and small creatures found in the different habitats; to say what similarities and differences they observe. If your school does not have access to extensive habitats, you can choose micro-habitats, eg under a stone, behind a shed. If it is extremely difficult to do any fieldwork use the B sheet instead. Ask children to consider how much water, shade and shelter there is as well as the variety of life present, including larger animals such as birds (in larger habitats) and smaller creatures found under stones or under water.

What the child does
The child studies three different habitats, eg a pond, a woodland area and part of the school field, records, using copymaster C41, what creatures are found in the habitats, and uses the reference books to identify, name and compare the creatures that have been found.

Key question
Does the child know that different livings things are found in different places?

Reassessment
Use copymaster C42 and get the children to draw the living things in their most likely habitats.

Level Description

Pupils use their knowledge of basic life processes, such as growth or reproduction, when they describe differences between living and non-living things. They provide simple explanations for changes in living things, such as diet affecting the health of humans or other animals, or lack of light or water altering plant growth. They identify ways in which an animal is suited to its environment, such as a fish having fins to help it swim.

TASK 10 — C43-44 — LIVING AND NON-LIVING THINGS A/B

Resources
Copymaster C43.

Organization
Each child works individually.

What you do
Give out copies of copymaster C43 and explain the task which is to colour blue everything that living things do. Discuss with the children the reasons for their choices.

What the child does
The child colours in blue the life processes that are common to all living things and explains the reasons for their choices to the teacher.

Key question
Does the child know the basic life processes common to all living things?

Reassessment
Use copymaster C44 to carry out the same exercise in a slightly different form. Remember that each living thing will not necessarily be able to do all the things coloured on C43.

TASK 11 — C45-46 — DIET AFFECTS THE HEALTH OF HUMANS A/B

Resources
Copymaster C45.

Organization
Each child works individually.

What you do
Give out copies of copymaster C45 and explain the task which is to name the four main food groups, identify foods that we should not eat too much of and say why and to plan a day's balanced menu.

What the child does
The child names the four main food groups (only being given a few letters including the initials), identifies the foods which we should not eat too much of and explains

why, and plans a day's healthy menu including food from the four main groups. The child may draw the menu.

Key question
Does the child know that we need to eat carefully to stay active and healthy?

Reassessment
Use copymaster C46 to identify the foods that give us energy (eg doughnuts, sugar, crisps), that are body building (contain proteins, eg sausages, ham, eggs), that are full of vitamins (fruit and vegetables), and those helping to clean out the body (eg that contain roughage, such as brown bread, Bran Flakes® and some fruit and vegetables). Point out that most foods are mixtures of the main nutrients, eg starch and protein.

TASK 12 — C47-48 — DIET AFFECTS TEETH A/B

Resources
Copymaster C47.

Organization
Each child works individually.

What you do
Give out copies of copymaster C47 and explain the task which is to identify those things that are good for teeth and those that are bad, to make a drawing of their own teeth including any with fillings, and to show with diagrams how sugar damages teeth. Explain that sugar remains in the saliva and produces acids that attack the enamel of the teeth and cause cavities.

What the child does
The child identifies the foods which may damage teeth, explains why the foods are damaging and what is found in foods that is bad for the teeth.

Key question
Does the child know that as a general rule we should avoid food containing high amounts of sugar to keep our teeth and gums healthy, although sugar-containing foods are essential to a healthy diet? Note that under certain circumstances a diabetic child may need to take sugar and they should not be made to feel that it is wrong to do so.

Reassessment
Use copymaster C48.

TASK 13 C49 -50 — EXERCISE AFFECTS THE HEALTH OF HUMANS A/B

Resources
Copymaster C49.

Organization
The work can be done individually or in pairs but monitor individual input.

What you do
Give out copies of copymaster C49 and explain the task which is to make a record of leisure activities throughout the week, tick the things the children do each day, write about whether they exercise enough to keep fit, suggest ways to improve their fitness.

What the child does
The child completes their own week's fitness log and investigates their own fitness.

Key question
Does the child know that we need sufficient exercise to stay fit and healthy?

Reassessment
Use copymaster C50 to retest the criteria for basic fitness.

TASK 14 C51 -52 — THE EFFECT OF WATER AND LIGHT ON PLANTS A/B

Resources
Copymaster C51, reference books.

Organization
Each child works individually.

What you do
Give out copies of copymaster C51 and explain the task which is to study the two illustrations and describe what will happen and why.

What the child does
The child completes the tasks on the copymaster.

Key question
Does the child know the conditions that affect plant growth?

Reassessment
Use copymaster C52. The task is to choose the pictures with the conditions that plant growth will require in order to continue. The child has to explain the reasons for the choices.

TASK 15 C53 -54 — EXPLORING HABITATS A/B

Resources
Copymaster C53.

Organization
Each child works individually.

What you do
Give out copies of copymaster C53 and discuss with the children how animals and plants may be suited to their environments. For example, in the case of the sunflower on the copymaster, it is suited to its environment because it can get sun and water and is out of the shade of the oak tree. Explain the task which is to say how the animals and plants on the copymaster are suited to their environments.

What the child does
The child gives reasons for the suitability of animals to their environments on the copymaster (the more reasons the better), or orally.

Key question
Can the child suggest reasons why animals are suited to their environments?

Reassessment
Use copymaster C54 with similar tasks.

AT3: Materials and their Properties

LEVEL 1

Level Description

Pupils know about a range of properties, such as texture or appearance, and they describe materials they observe in terms of these properties.

TASK 1

C55 -56

DESCRIBE MATERIALS A/B

Resources
Samples of wool, wood, silk, toffee stick, and copymaster C55.

Organization
Each child works individually.

What you do
Let the children handle the items specified above, describe them as part of a class or group introduction. Draw attention to the words used, before giving out the copymaster. Give out copymaster C55 and explain the task which is to link the materials to their descriptions by drawing arrows. Help the children to read the descriptions of the materials if necessary, explain some words, eg flexible, rigid, etc and encourage the use of a wide vocabulary. Allow children to examine and feel the above materials as they use the copymaster.

What the child does
The child feels the different materials and links each one to its description on the copymaster using arrows.

Key question
Does the child know a range of properties (eg texture, appearance) and can they use these to describe materials?

Reassessment
Use copymaster C56 which includes the same task but uses different materials (metal, plastic, stone, rubber).

TASK 2

C57 -58

DESCRIBE MATERIALS BY THEIR PROPERTIES A/B

Resources
Samples of rough and smooth materials such as a concrete block, sandpaper, glass, pieces of rough wood (bark), card, nail brushes, the school pet, copymaster C57.

Organization
Each child works individually.

What you do
Encourage children to examine and feel the materials. Give out copies of copymaster C58 and explain the task which is to link the materials on the copymaster with the words smooth or rough by using arrows.

What the child does
The child feels the different materials and links each one to either smooth or rough drawing arrows on the copymaster.

Key question
Does the child know a range of different materials can have similar qualities?

Reassessment
Use copymaster C58 with flexible and rigid materials such as plastic rulers, bows, rubbers, headbands, pencils, broom handles, pen lids, table tops, frying pans.

Level Description

Pupils identify a range of common materials and know about some of their properties. They describe similarities and differences between materials. They sort materials into groups and describe in everyday terms, such as shininess, hardness or smoothness, the basis for their groupings. They describe ways in which some materials are changed by heating or cooling or by processes such as bending or stretching.

TASK 3 — C59-60

IDENTIFY MATERIALS BY THEIR PROPERTIES A/B

Resources
Copymaster C59, balsa, tissue paper, tracing paper, wallpaper, rubber bands, corrugated plastic, aluminium cans, copper tubing, sandstone, pebbles, coal, clear glass, clay.

Organization
Each child works individually.

What you do
Give out copies of copymaster C59 and explain the task which is to identify the materials and link them to their properties (there may be more than one). Show the children the range of materials. Explain any unfamiliar terms and relate them to ones they know such as hard and rigid.

What the child does
The child identifies the common materials and ticks their properties (eg rigid or flexible) in the appropriate boxes on the copymaster.

Key question
Can the child identify common materials and do they know their properties?

Reassessment
Use copymaster C60 and a range of materials such as hardwood, plain paper, thick card, corrugated card, rubber, plastic bags, plastic tubes, lead, tin foil, chalk, bricks, concrete, opaque glass, china. The task is the same as on C59.

TASK 4 — C61-62

DESCRIBE SIMILARITIES AND DIFFERENCES A/B

Resources
Copymaster C61, cotton and wool, silk and rubber, aluminium and copper, brick and wood, coal and chalk, water and custard

Organization
Each child works individually.

What you do
Encourage the children to examine the materials in terms of their properties, eg smell, flexibility, stretchiness, change of state (solid, liquid or gas), hardness, transparency. Give out copies of copymaster C61 and explain the task which is to write down the similarities between the pairs of materials and to list the differences in the outer columns of the copymaster.

What the child does
The child examines the materials in terms of their properties, writes down the similarities between the two named materials in the centre column and lists the differences in the outer columns.

Key question
Can the child describe similarities and differences between materials?

Reassessment
Use copymaster C62. The task is the same as on C61 but with different materials.

TASK 5 — C63-64

SORTING MATERIALS A/B

Resources
Copymaster C63.

Organization
The children work in pairs or small groups.

What you do
As part of a group or class introduction, talk about the everyday terms that may be used to describe the properties of materials, such as hard, rigid, transparent. Give out copies of copymaster C63 and explain the task which is to walk round the inside of the school and notice eight different parts of the school such as window frame, doors; to list these on the copymaster and to write down what they are made of; to complete the copymaster and group the materials explaining how they were sorted. Take the children round the school building (inside) and encourage them to look at walls, floors, windows, ceilings, beams, partitions, etc.

What the child does
The child walks round the inside of the school and identifies some of the materials used in its construction, eg wood, plastic, metal and glass, and groups these materials by their similar properties.

Key question
Can the child sort materials into groups using everyday terms?

Reassessment
Use copymaster C64 and explore the materials to be found outside the school buildings; group them as on C63.

TASK 6 — C65-66 — CHANGES IN MATERIALS A/B

Resources
Copymaster C65, candles, water, Back Ton® oven clay (this clay can be fired at 150 °C in an ordinary oven, available from NES Arnold), jelly, custard, raw eggs, saucepans, cooker, freezer, matches.

Organization
Each child works individually.

What you do
Give out copies of copymaster C65 and explain the task which is to make drawings of what happens to the materials when they are heated and cooled; encourage close observation and accurate drawings with coloured pencils. Demonstrate the heating and cooling of the materials.

What the child does
The child uses pictures or words to record the effects of heating or cooling on the materials listed on the copymaster.

Key question
Can the child describe the ways that some materials change due to being heated or cooled?

Reassessment
Use copymaster C66. The task is to record the effect of bending and stretching on materials such as Plasticine®, dough, soap, a stick of rock, wool, a rubber.

LEVEL 3

Level Description

Pupils use their knowledge and understanding of materials when they describe a variety of ways of sorting them into groups according to their properties. They explain why some materials are particularly suitable for specific purposes, such as metal for making electric cables. They recognise that some changes, such as the freezing of water, can be reversed and some, such as the baking of clay, cannot, and they classify changes in this way.

TASK 7 — C67-68 — SORTING MATERIALS BY THEIR PROPERTIES A/B

Resources
Copymaster C67, metal rulers, glass mixing bowls, wooden spoons, rubber balls, pencils, metal spoons, tin cans, nails, oranges, rubber Wellingtons, glass vases, metal spring.

Organization
Each child works individually.

What you do
Give out copies of copymaster C67 and explain the task which is to suggest and record how many ways materials can be sorted, choose one way and make a diagram of the groupings and explain reasons for their choices. Show the children the materials and suggest ways of sorting them, eg into rigid and flexible materials. Ask how many other ways they can find to sort them.

What the child does
The child examines the materials and suggests ways for sorting them, chooses their own way of sorting and draws the materials in groups on the copymaster and explains the reasons for their decisions.

Key question
Can the child sort the materials according to their properties?

Reassessment
Use copymaster C68; the same task but different materials such as woollen jumpers, cotton T-shirts, woollen socks, leather shoes, leather belts, cotton hats, canvas coats, plastic Wellingtons, nylon tights, woollen bobble hats.

TASK 8 — C69-70 — SUITABLE MATERIALS A/B

Resources
Copymaster C69, non-metal objects (eg rubbers, felt-tip pens), metal objects (eg paperclips, scissors), bulbs, wires, batteries, crocodile clips.

Organization
Each child works individually.

What you do
Give the children copies of copymaster C69 and explain the task which is to identify which objects are suitable for conducting electricity and to say why wire is used in electrical circuits.

What the child does

The child identifies materials which are suitable for conducting electricity, explains why wire is used in electrical circuits.

Key question

Can the child say why metal is suitable to be used in an electric cable.

Reassessment

Use copymaster C70 and different materials such as plastic spoons, metal spoons, metal rulers, oranges, bulbs, wires, batteries, crocodile clips. The task is to identify which objects are suitable for conducting electricity and to explain which material is best for making electrical circuits and why.

TASK 9 — C71-72
REVERSIBLE/ IRREVERSIBLE CHANGES A/B

Resources

Copymaster C71, tap water, ice-cube tray, freezer, thermometers (Celsius), saucers, bowls, jugs and a kettle.

Organization

Children work in groups with close adult supervision for safety. This is a demanding but rewarding activity.

What you do

Give out copies of copymaster C71 and explain the task which is to investigate the states of water, find out if changes can be reversed and to complete the copymaster. Encourage correct use of scientific terminology such as condense, evaporate and freeze. Encourage fair testing.

What the child does

The child measures the temperature of tap water, pours some water into an ice-tray and lets it freeze. As it freezes the child measures the temperature again. When ice is formed they empty it into a bowl and periodically measure the temperature of the ice as it melts again. The child heats water in the kettle with adult help and measures the temperature as it boils. The child collects condensed steam on a cold surface.

Key question

Does the child know that freezing water is reversible?

Reassessment

Give out copies of the copymaster C72 and explain the task which is to observe eggs in four different conditions and make drawings to show the differences; to explain what has happened to the eggs as they cook. Boil the eggs and cut them in half so that the children can observe the differences. Discuss with the children whether or not the boiling of eggs can be reversed.

The child makes simple observations, looking at the four different eggs, and draws a raw egg and eggs boiled for 1, 3 and 7 minutes paying particular attention to the differences between them.

TASK 10 — C73-74
NATURAL AND MADE MATERIALS A/B

Resources

Copymaster C73, a variety of made and natural materials for class discussion.

Organization

The children take part in a class discussion and then each child completes the copymaster.

What you do

Give out copies of copymaster C73 and explain the task which is to identify the made and natural materials shown on the copymaster.

What the child does

The child completes the tasks.

Key question

Can the child identify natural and made materials?

Reassessment

Use copymaster C74 which includes different materials to sort into natural and made groups.

TASK 11 — C75-76
MASS AND SIZE OF MATERIALS A/B

Resources

Copymaster C75, Plasticine® or dough, weighing machines.

Organization

Each child works individually.

What you do

Give out copies of copymaster C75 and explain the task which is to say whether or not a snake, a car, an apple and a cat will all weigh the same when each is made from pieces of Plasticine® each of which weigh the same; to test their ideas and draw conclusions about mass and size of materials.

What the child does

The child makes predictions, makes the models, tests the predictions and draws conclusions.

Key question

Does the child know that even though a material may be stretched or change state its mass is unchanged?

Reassessment

Use copymaster C76 and six ice-cubes to determine whether the weight of water contained in six ice-cubes is the same as the weight of water produced when the six ice-cubes are melted.

AT4: Physical Processes

LEVEL 1

Level Description

Pupils describe the changes in light, sound or movement, which result from actions such as switching on a simple electrical circuit, or pushing and pulling objects. They recognise that sound and light come from a variety of sources and name some of these sources.

TASK 1
C77 -78

DESCRIBE CHANGES IN LIGHT A/B

Resources
Copymaster C77, bulbs, wires, batteries.

Organization
Each child works individually.

What you do
Give children copies of copymaster C77 and explain the task which is to say what will happen to the lights as the changes to the circuit shown on the copymaster are made. Ask the children to colour the bulbs yellow when they will light up in the circuits shown on the copymaster.

What the child does
The child completes the task on the copymaster and tests.

Key question
Can the child describe changes in light resulting from switching on a simple circuit?

Reassessment
Use copymaster C78 which includes three different circuits.

TASK 2
C79 -80

DESCRIBE CHANGES IN SOUND A/B

Resources
Copymaster C79.

Organization
Each child works individually.

What you do
Give out copies of copymaster C79 and explain the task which is to colour blue the objects which make a loud sound and to colour red the objects which make a soft sound.

What the child does
The child tries out the objects and colours blue the objects which make a loud sound and red the objects which make a soft sound.

Key question
Does the child understand that objects can make loud or soft sounds?

Reassessment
Use copymaster C80 which includes different objects.

TASK 3
C81 -82

PUSHING AND PULLING OBJECTS A/B

Resources
Copymaster C81.

Organization
Each child works individually.

What you do
Give out copies of the copymaster and explain the task which is to look at the illustrations on the copymaster and describe by talking the changes in movement that result from the pushing and pulling actions. Make a note of the children's descriptions of what is happening on the copymaster. The children should use the words 'push' and 'pull' in their descriptions.

What the child does
The child looks at the illustrations on the copymaster and describes to the teacher the changes in movement that result from the pushing and pulling actions shown, using the words 'push' and 'pull'.

Key question
Does the child understand that things can be moved by pushing or pulling them?

Reassessment
Use copymaster C82 which contains illustrations of different actions.

TASK 4
C83 -84

IDENTIFY AND NAME LIGHT SOURCES A/B

Resources
Copymaster C83.

Organization
Each child works individually.

What you do
Give out copies of copymaster C83 and explain the task which is to identify sources of light in the illustration of a day street scene by circling them.

What the child does
The child completes the tasks, draws circles around each light source and names them by linking them with the correct word.

Key question
Can the child identify sources of light?

Reassessment
Use copymaster C84 with the same task but illustrating a night scene.

TASK 5
C85 -86

IDENTIFY AND NAME SOUND SOURCES A/B

Resources
Copymaster C85.

Organization
Each child works individually.

What you do
Give out copies of copymaster C85 and explain the task which is to circle the places where sound comes from.

What the child does
The child completes the tasks.

Key question
Can the child identify sources of sound?

Reassessment
Use copymaster C86 which contains the same task but illustrates different activities.

LEVEL 2

Level Description

Pupils know about a range of physical phenomena and recognise and describe similarities and differences associated with them. They compare the way in which devices, such as bulbs, work in different electrical circuits. They compare the effects of similar phenomena, such as brightness or colour of lights, or the loudness or pitch of sounds. They compare the movement of different objects in terms of speed or direction.

TASK 6
C87 -88

HOW BULBS WORK A/B

Resources
Copymaster C87.

Organization
Each child works individually.

What you do
Give out copies of the copymaster and explain the task which is to colour the bulbs of circuits in which the bulb will light.

What the child does
The child colours the bulbs in the diagrams of circuits in which the bulb will light.

Key question
Does the child know how bulbs work in electrical circuits?

Reassessment
Use copymaster C88 on which the child shows which circuit is complete by colouring the bulb if it will light up and they describe what is happening in the completed circuit.

TASK 7
C89 -90

SOUNDS A/B

Resources
Copymaster C89 which shows various musical instruments.

Organization
The children work in groups but monitor individual input.

What you do

Ask the child to investigate what sounds can be made by striking, blowing, shaking and plucking. Give out copies of copymaster C89 and explain the task which is to identify how sound is produced by each musical instrument illustrated and to link them to the correct words.

What the child does

The child investigates different ways of making sounds and completes the task on the copymaster.

Key question

Does the child know that different types of musical instruments can produce a variety of sounds? Does the child know that sounds are produced by vibrating objects?

Reassessment

Use copymaster C90 which includes illustrations of different ways to make sound. Encourage the children to use appropriate vocabulary to explain. The children could also work in groups to make sound effects for a story to be recorded and played to the school.

TASK 8
C91 -92

COMPARE MOVEMENT – DIRECTION/SPEED A/B

Resources

Toy cars, ramps, sand, obstructions (barriers) copymaster C91.

Organization

Each child works individually.

What you do

Encourage the children to use toy cars and try out ways of starting and stopping them. Give out copies of the copymaster and explain the task which is to draw two diagrams showing how to start a toy car moving (without using their hands); to draw two ways of stopping the toy car moving (without using their hands) and to answer the questions on the copymaster. Ask questions and encourage children to think of ways to stop and start a toy car (eg start it by pushing or putting it on a ramp; stop it by using an obstruction or an escape road made of sand). Encourage them to vary the force applied by asking questions such as 'Does the car travel further if you push it harder? How can you make it travel further?'.

What the child does

The child establishes as many ways as they can of starting and stopping a toy car and records these on copymaster C91.

Key question

Can the child explain how the movement of an object can be altered?

Reassessment

Use copymaster C92 to repeat the tasks by using a ball instead of a toy car.

LEVEL 3

Level Description

Pupils use their knowledge and understanding to link cause and effect in simple explanations of physical phenomena, such as a bulb failing to light because of a break in an electrical circuit, or the direction or speed of movement of an object changing because of a force applied to it. They begin to make simple generalisations about physical phenomena, such as explaining that sounds they hear become fainter the further they are from the source.

TASK 9
C93 -94

LIGHT FAILS BECAUSE OF BREAK IN CIRCUIT A/B

Resources

Copymaster C93, bulbs, wires, batteries, crocodile clips.

Organization

Each child works individually.

What you do

Give out copies of copymaster C93 and explain the task which is to predict, try out and record results (say whether the bulbs in the given circuits will light up or remain unlit). Encourage predictions and careful observation of where the wires touch the bulb.

What the child does

The child predicts, tries out and records (writes down whether or not the bulb will light on the illustrated circuits and explains why).

Key question

Does the child know why a bulb will not light and why it will light? Can the child explain their reasoning with diagrams if necessary?

Reassessment

Use copymaster C94 to complete similar tasks but with different circuits.

TASK 10
C95 -96

APPLIED FORCES AFFECT DIRECTION/ SPEED A/B

Resources

Copymasters C95.

Organization
Each child works individually.

What you do
Give out copies of copymaster C95 and explain the task which is to draw arrows on the diagrams to show what will happen to the objects in the pictures (this can be done with a demonstration of an example) and to explain why. Encourage the children to explain their answers and give reasons.

What the child does
The child explains where the forces are acting in the pictures and draws arrows to show what will happen to the objects.

Key question
Can the child explain how and why the speed or direction of an object changes when a force is applied to it?

Reassessment
Use copymaster C96.

11 SIDEWAYS PUSHES/ PULLS CAUSE SWERVES A/B

TASK 11
C97 -98

Resources
Copymaster C97.

Organization
Each children can work as a class or individually.

What you do
Give out copies of copymaster C97 and explain the task which is to study carefully the illustrations and describe using words and arrows on the copymaster which direction the ball will take after glancing off the defender's shoulder. Encourage the children to use words such as 'swerve, deflection, forces'. (It is difficult to demonstrate this but you could try practical sessions with children in the playground to show how footballs can swerve away from the original line of flight when deflected – discuss with diagrams back in class.) Allow the children to explain their answers and give reasons.

What the child does
The child explains where the forces are acting in the pictures and draw arrows to show what will happen to the objects when they are deflected.

Key question
Can the child explain how and why the direction of an object changes when a sideways force is applied to it?

Reassessment
Use copymaster C98 which includes similar tasks but different illustrations.

12 PULLS/PUSHES CAN CHANGE SOME SHAPES A/B

TASK 12
C99 -100

Resources
Copymaster C99, balloons, Plasticine® or clay, rubber bands, small cricket bats (or similar thing for hitting soft materials).

Organization
The children can work as a class or individually.

What you do
Have a practical session with the children poking balloons, pressing, pulling or hitting the clay and stretching elastic bands. Discuss what is happening when the forces are applied to the soft materials. Give out copies of copymaster C99 and explain the task which is to say what they think will happen in the illustrations.

What the child does
The child makes drawings of what happens in each case, explains where the forces are acting in the pictures by labelling and using arrows to show what happens to the objects when hit, pushed, stretched, squeezed or pulled.

Key question
Can the child explain how and why the shape of a soft object changes when forces are applied to it?

Reassessment
Use copymaster C100.

13 SOUNDS BECOME LOUDER A/B

TASK 13
C101 -102

Resources
Copymaster C101.

Organization
Each child works individually.

What you do
Give out copies of copymaster C101 and explain the task which is to say which sound will be the louder and which the quieter by drawing a circle round the louder (in one case the child should circle both as they are equidistant from the hearer).

What the child does
The child completes the copymaster.

Key question
Does the child understand that sounds become fainter the further you move from the source?

Reassessment
Use copymaster C102.

Name: _____ Date: _____

A | Describe features of living things

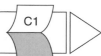

Draw a picture of your fruit

My fruit is a _____

Use a magnifying glass and draw a seed

This is my seed

Colour these fruits the right colours and name them

This is an _____

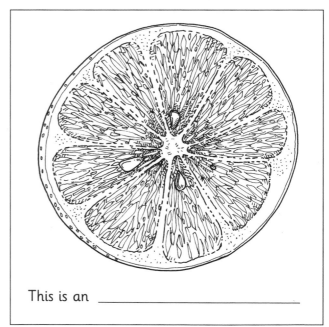

This is an _____

• •

Child's oral description (words used):

Name: _____ Date: _____

B Describe features of living things

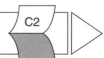

C2

Draw a picture of your vegetable

My vegetable is a _____

Draw your vegetable cut in half

This is my vegetable cut in half

Colour these vegetables the right colours and name them

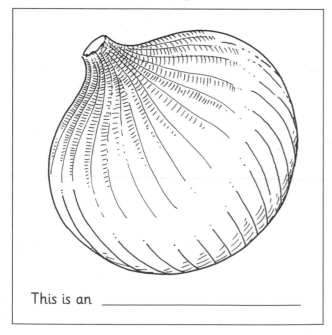

This is an _____

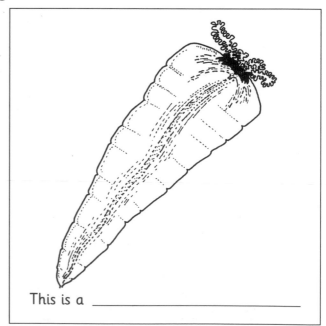

This is a _____

Child's oral description (words used):

Name: _____ Date: _____

A | Describe simple features of objects

Which objects does a magnet pick up?
Colour red those that are picked up
Colour the others green

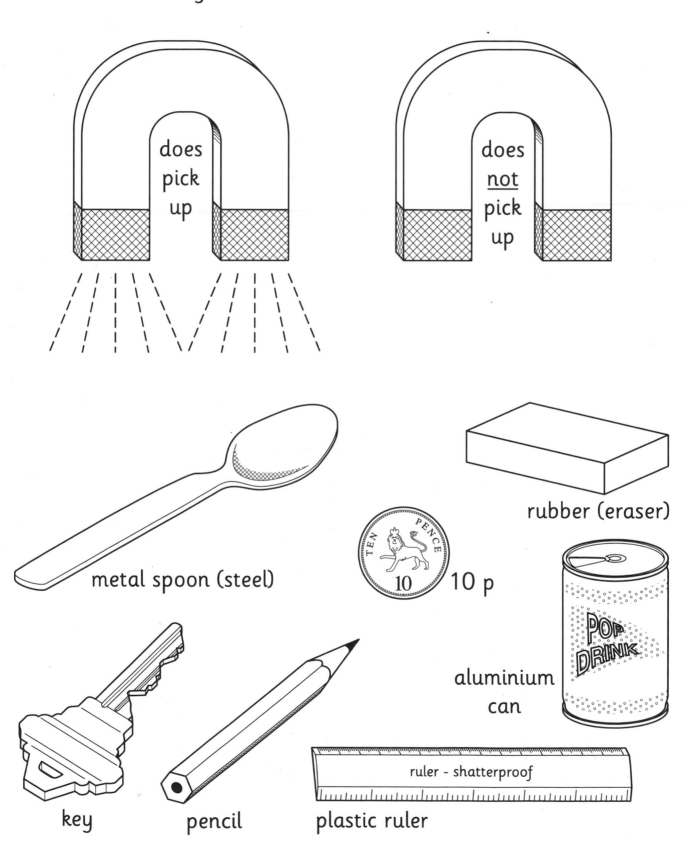

does pick up

does <u>not</u> pick up

metal spoon (steel)

10 p

rubber (eraser)

aluminium can

key

pencil

ruler - shatterproof

plastic ruler

B | Describe simple features of objects

Which objects does a magnet pick up?
Colour red those that are picked up
Colour the others green

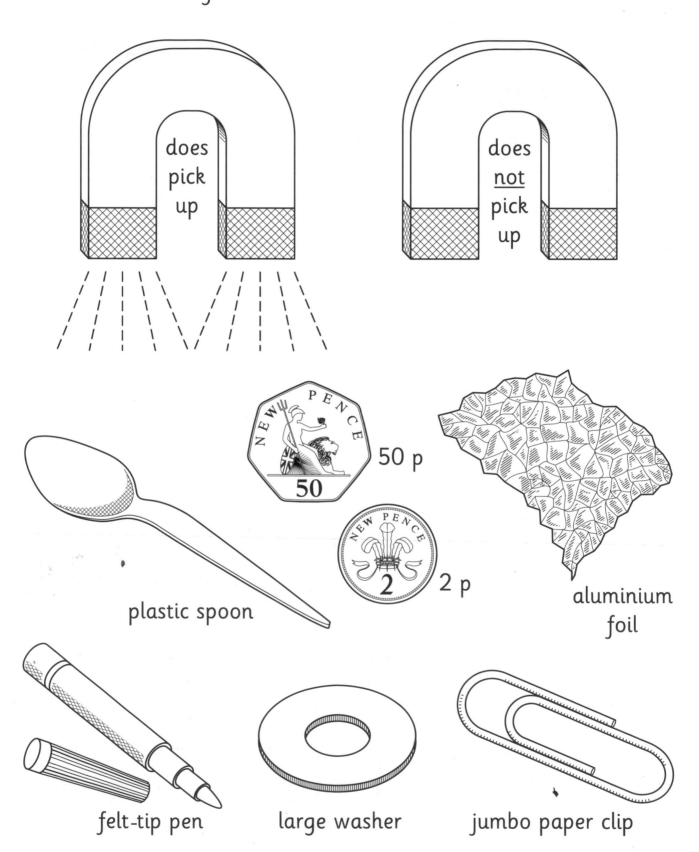

does pick up

does not pick up

plastic spoon

50 p

2 p

aluminium foil

felt-tip pen

large washer

jumbo paper clip

A | Describe simple features of animals

C5

What colour are these animals?
Colour them carefully
Talk about them and name them

• •

Child's oral description (words used):

Name: _____ Date: _____

| B | Describe simple features of animals | 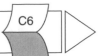 |

What colour are these animals?

Colour them carefully

Talk about them and name them

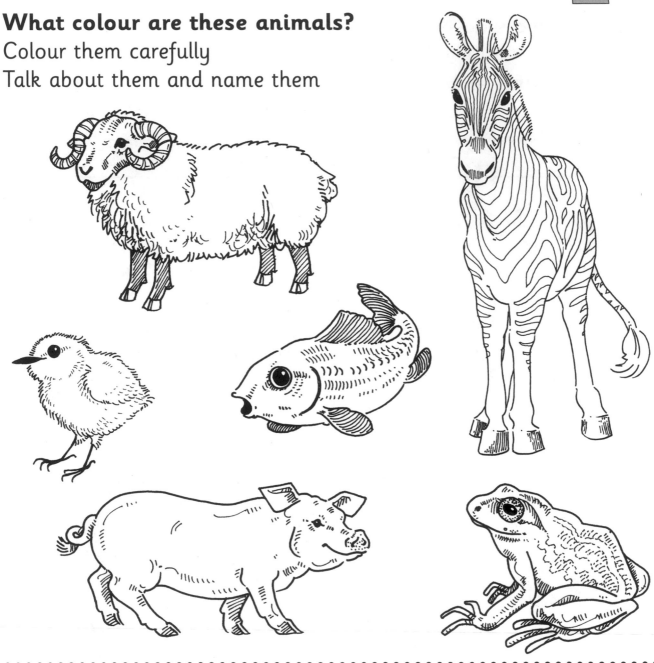

∙ ∙

Child's oral description (words used):

Name: _____ Date: _____

| A | Respond to suggestions, predict | C7 |

Which objects do you think you could see through?

Test them and record your results with ticks

Object/Material	I predict	Can see through clearly	Can see through a bit	Cannot see through at all
a brick	I predict			
	Tested			
a coloured bottle	I predict			
	Tested			
thick card	I predict			
	Tested			
tracing paper	I predict			
	Tested			
black polythene	I predict			
	Tested			

Name: _____ Date: _____

| B | Respond to suggestions, predict | C8 |

Which objects do you think you could see through?

Test them and record your results with ticks

Object/Material	I predict Tested	Can see through clearly	Can see through a bit	Cannot see through at all
wood 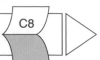	I predict			
	Tested			
coloured water	I predict			
	Tested			
a leaf	I predict			
	Tested			
curtain fabric	I predict			
	Tested			
clean water	I predict			
	Tested			

Name: _____ Date: _____

A Respond to and make suggestions

Look at the picture
Which car do you think will travel furthest?
Tick your choice

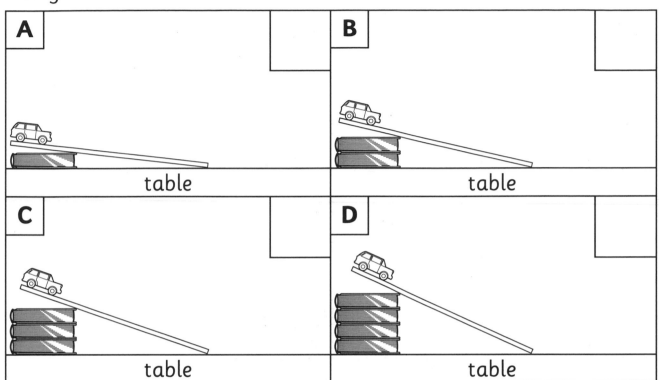

A   table

B   table

C   table

D   table

Investigate
Find out how far each will go

A car went _____ cm along the table

B car went _____ cm along the table

C car went _____ cm along the table

D car went _____ cm along the table

Which car went the furthest? _____

Is this what you expected? _____

Why do you think it went the furthest? _____

_____

_____

_____

Name: _____ Date: _____

B │ Respond to and make suggestions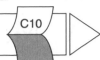

Look at the picture
Which ball do you think will travel furthest?
Tick your choice

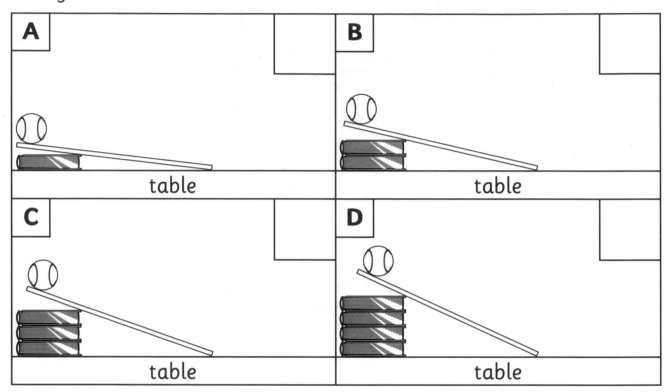

A

table

B

table

C

table

D

table

Investigate
Find out how far each will go

A ball went _____ cm along the table

B ball went _____ cm along the table

C ball went _____ cm along the table

D ball went _____ cm along the table

Which ball went the furthest? _____

Is this what you expected? _____

Why do you think it went the furthest? _____

_____

_____

Name: _____ Date: _____

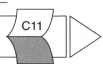

A Make suggestions, draw conclusions

Colour blue what you think will dissolve
Colour red what you think will not dissolve

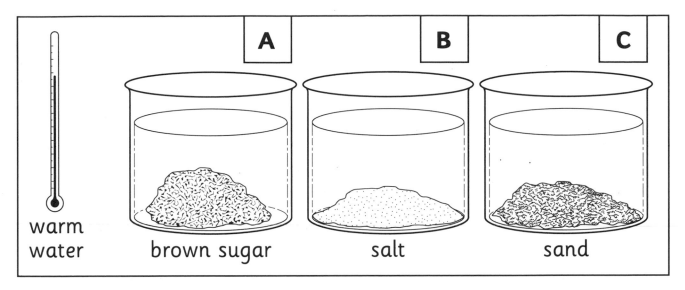

Stir each for the same time. Watch what happens.
Record the time it takes to dissolve each substance.
Draw in any substances that did not dissolve.

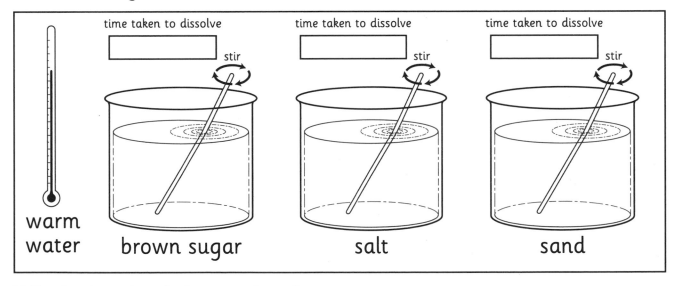

Which dissolved the quickest? _____

Is this what you expected? _____

Why do you think this happened? _____

_____

_____

Name: _____ Date: _____

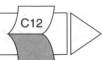

| B | Make suggestions, draw conclusions |

Colour blue what you think will dissolve
Colour red what you think will not dissolve

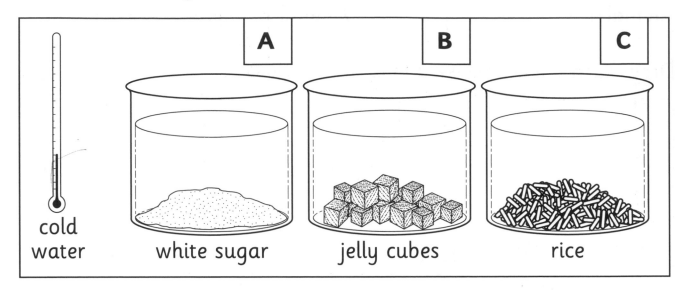

cold water   white sugar   jelly cubes   rice

Stir each for the same time. Watch what happens.
Record the time it takes each to dissolve.
Draw in any substances that did not dissolve.

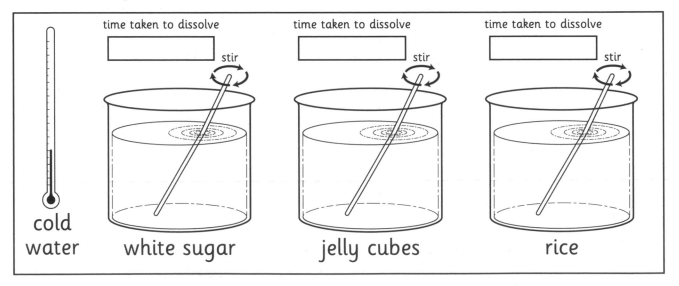

time taken to dissolve   stir   time taken to dissolve   stir   time taken to dissolve   stir

cold water   white sugar   jelly cubes   rice

Which dissolved the quickest? _____

Is this what you expected? _____

Why do you think this happened? _____

_____

_____

Name: _____ Date: _____

A Compare living things

The two animals I have chosen to compare are:

Animal 1 _____ Animal 2 _____

Draw each creature. Use a magnifying glass.

Animal 1	Animal 2

Write down their similarities and their differences

The same	Different

Name: _____ Date: _____

B | Compare living things

The two animals I have chosen to compare are:

Animal 1 _____ Animal 2 _____

Draw each creature. Use a magnifying glass.

Animal 1	Animal 2

Write down their similarities and their differences

The same	Different

Name: _____ Date: _____

A	Compare events

Try to dissolve one teaspoonful of these

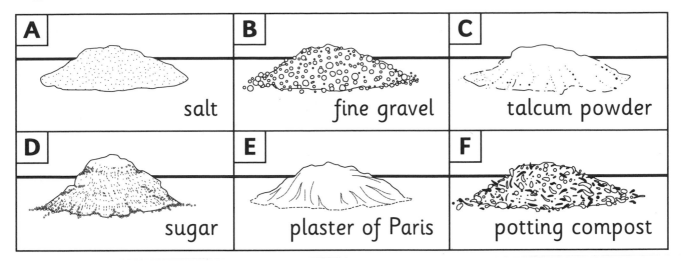

A	**B**	**C**
salt	fine gravel	talcum powder
D	**E**	**F**
sugar	plaster of Paris	potting compost

Stir each into the same amount of water

Record what happens

Dissolved	Floated	Sank	Became solid

How did you measure the water? _____

_____

_____

Which dissolved the quickest? _____

Why do you think this was? _____

_____

B | Compare events

C16

Try to dissolve one teaspoonful of these

A	B	C
baking powder	bath crystals	wood chippings
D	**E**	**F**
flour	sand	coffee powder

Stir each into the same amount of water

Record what happens

Dissolved	Floated	Sank	Became lumpy/creamy

How did you measure the water? _____

_____

_____

_____

Which dissolved the quickest? _____

Why do you think this was? _____

_____

Name: _____ Date: _____

A Compare objects

Join the objects to words that describe them

(You can join objects to more than one word)

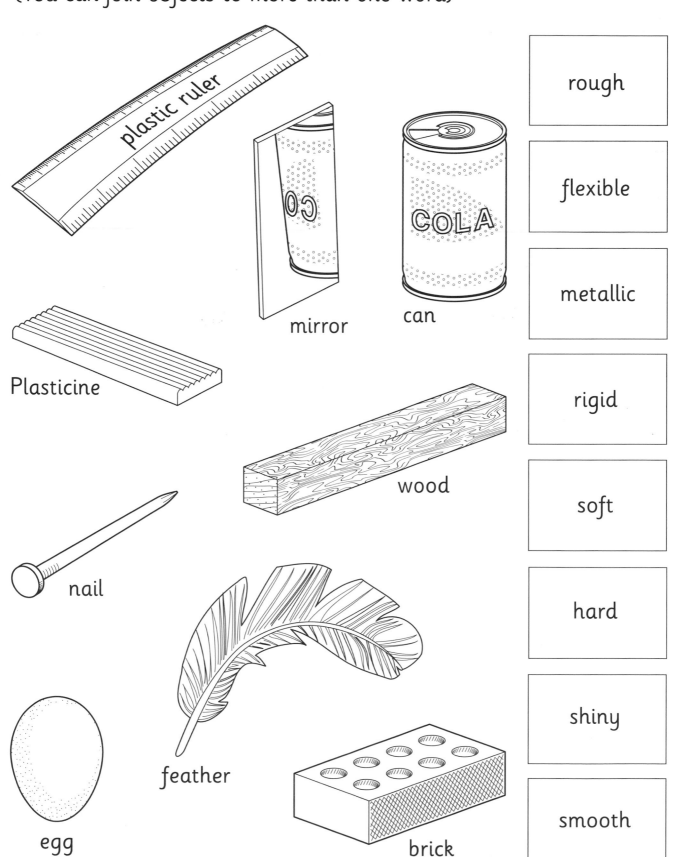

plastic ruler

mirror

can

Plasticine

wood

nail

feather

egg

brick

rough

flexible

metallic

rigid

soft

hard

shiny

smooth

Name: _____   Date: _____

| B | Comparing objects |

Join the objects to words that describe them
(You can join objects to more than one word)

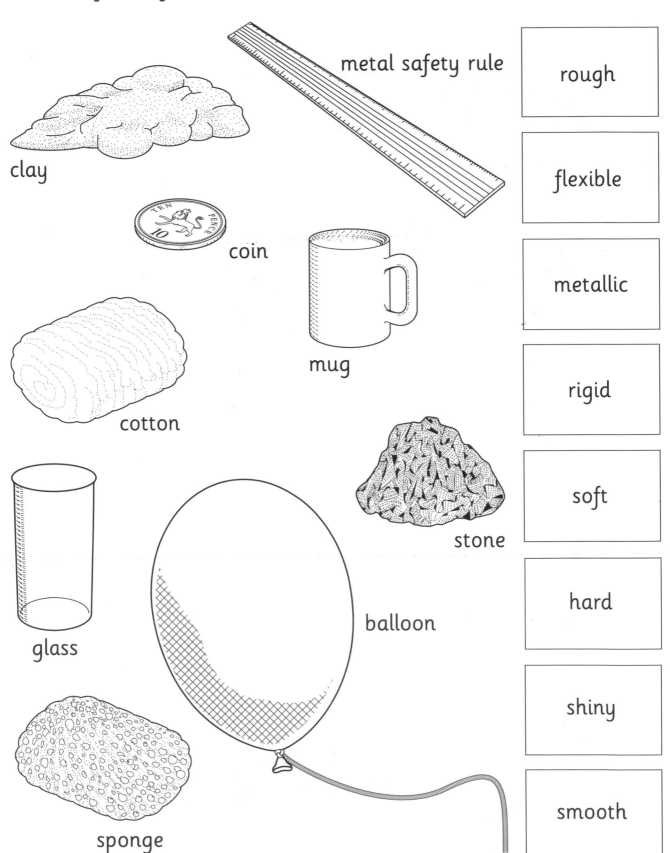

metal safety rule

clay

coin

mug

cotton

stone

glass

balloon

sponge

rough

flexible

metallic

rigid

soft

hard

shiny

smooth

Name: _____ Date: _____

| A | Make predictions, record observations | C19 |

Which ball will bounce the highest when dropped from 1 metre?
Tick ✓ your choice

Which ball will bounce the lowest when dropped from 1 metre?
Cross ✗ your choice

| A golf ball | B tennis ball |
| C table tennis ball | D cricket ball |

Test them
The one that bounced highest was _____
      It bounced _____ cm
The one that bounced lowest was _____
      It bounced _____ cm

Is this what you expected? _____

Can you think of a reason why this happened? _____

_____

_____

Name: _____ Date: _____

B | Make predictions, record observations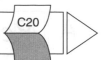

Which ball will bounce the highest when dropped from 1 metre?

Tick ✓ your choice

Which ball will bounce the lowest when dropped from 1 metre?

Cross ✗ your choice

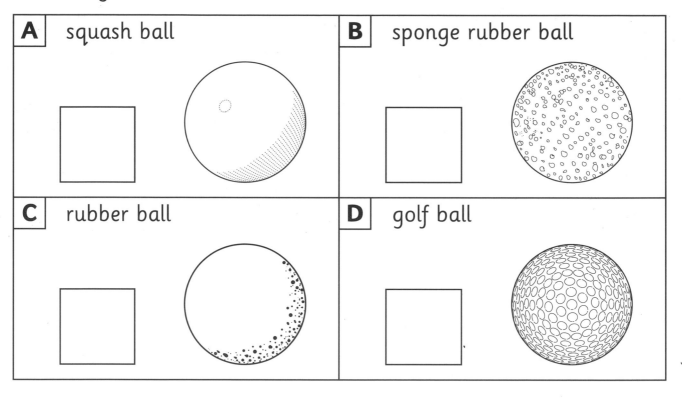

| A squash ball | B sponge rubber ball |
| C rubber ball | D golf ball |

Test them

The one that bounced highest was _____

It bounced _____ cm

The one that bounced lowest was _____

It bounced _____ cm

Is this what you expected? _____

Can you think of a reason why this happened? _____

_____

_____

Name: _____ Date: _____

A │ Record observations, make predictions ◁ C21 ▷

I think that

wool   **plastic**   **paper**

will keep the water warmest (Circle your choice)

I think this because _____

Test them (Record your results in the chart)

material wound around beaker	temperature recorded (°Celsius)					
	at start	after 15 mins	after 10 mins	after 15 mins	after 20 mins	**total temp drop**
wool						
plastic						
paper						

Draw a bar graph to show how the temperature of water in each beaker varied after 20 minutes

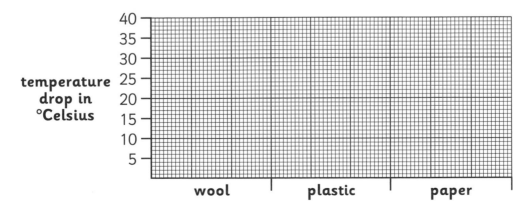

What did you find out from your experiment? _____

_____

_____

_____

Name: _____ Date: _____

| B | Record observations, make predictions | C22 |

I think that

polythene   canvas   wool

will be the most waterproof material (Circle your choice)

Record your results in this table

material type over beaker	Amount of water that ran into the beaker after 10 minutes (in ml)
polythene	
wool	
nylon	

Draw a bar graph to show how much water each material let through after 10 minutes

amount of water let through after 10 minutes (in ml)

polythene   wool   nylon

What did you find out from your experiment? _____

_____

_____

Is this what you thought would happen? _____

_____

Name: _____ Date: _____

| A | Fair test with help |

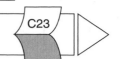

The pictures show two sets of experiments to find out
how much different threads and ropes stretch.
Each piece starts the same length.

Which set do you think is a fair test? Why?

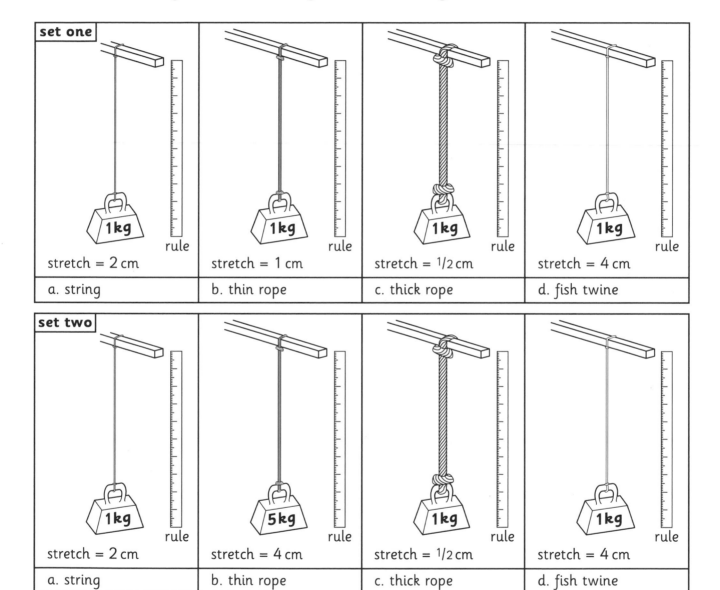

set one

a. string	b. thin rope	c. thick rope	d. fish twine
1kg rule	1kg rule	1kg rule	1kg rule
stretch = 2 cm	stretch = 1 cm	stretch = 1/2 cm	stretch = 4 cm

set two

a. string	b. thin rope	c. thick rope	d. fish twine
1kg rule	5kg rule	1kg rule	1kg rule
stretch = 2 cm	stretch = 4 cm	stretch = 1/2 cm	stretch = 4 cm

I think that set _____ is a fair test because _____

_____

_____

_____

_____

Name: _____ Date: _____

| B | Fair test with help |

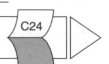

C24

The pictures show two sets of experiments to find out
how much different threads and ropes stretch.
Each time, the same weight is used to stretch the different threads.

Which set do you think is a fair test? Why?

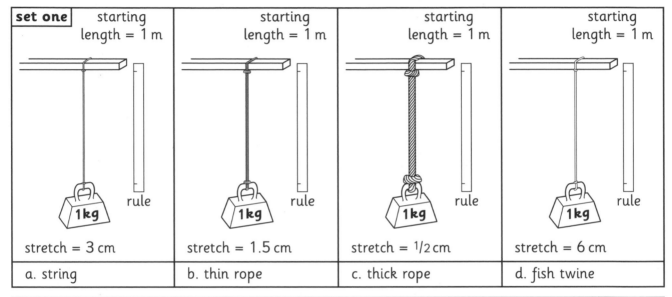

set one starting length = 1 m	starting length = 1 m	starting length = 1 m	starting length = 1 m
stretch = 3 cm	stretch = 1.5 cm	stretch = 1/2 cm	stretch = 6 cm
a. string	b. thin rope	c. thick rope	d. fish twine

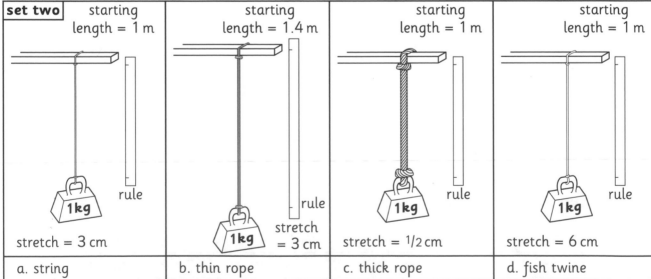

set two starting length = 1 m	starting length = 1.4 m	starting length = 1 m	starting length = 1 m
stretch = 3 cm	stretch = 3 cm	stretch = 1/2 cm	stretch = 6 cm
a. string	b. thin rope	c. thick rope	d. fish twine

I think that set _____ is a fair test because _____

_____

_____

_____

Name: _____ Date: _____

| A | Recognize and name parts of the body |

Draw arrows to connect the correct name to body parts

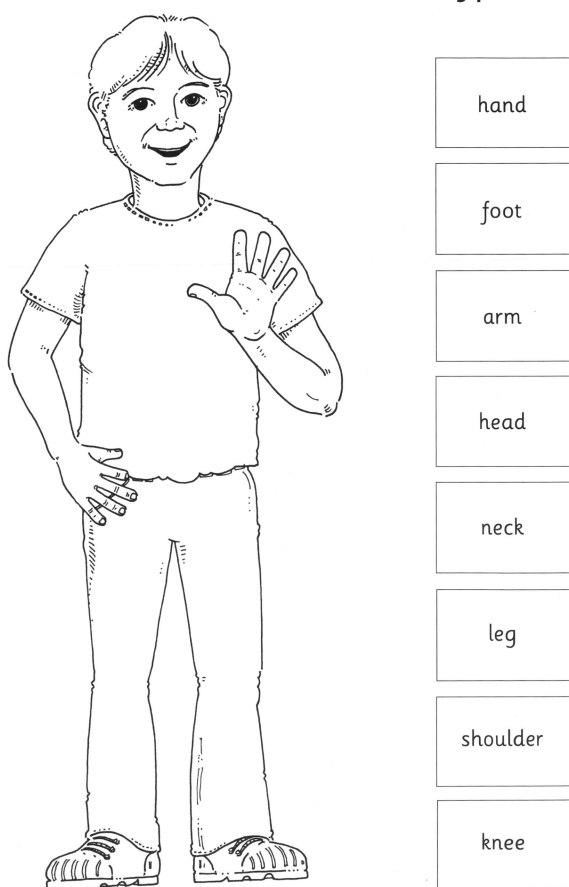

hand

foot

arm

head

neck

leg

shoulder

knee

B | Recognize and name parts of the body C26

Draw arrows to connect the correct name to body parts

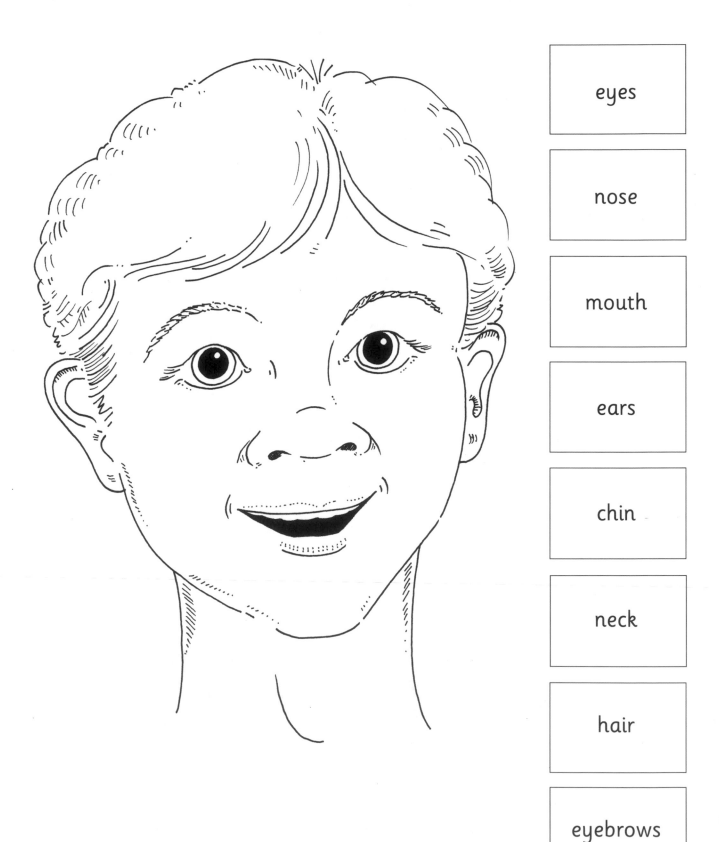

| eyes |

| nose |

| mouth |

| ears |

| chin |

| neck |

| hair |

| eyebrows |

Name: _____ Date: _____

A | Recognize and name parts of plants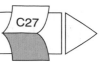

Draw arrows to join the correct names to parts of the plant

leaf

petal

stem

roots

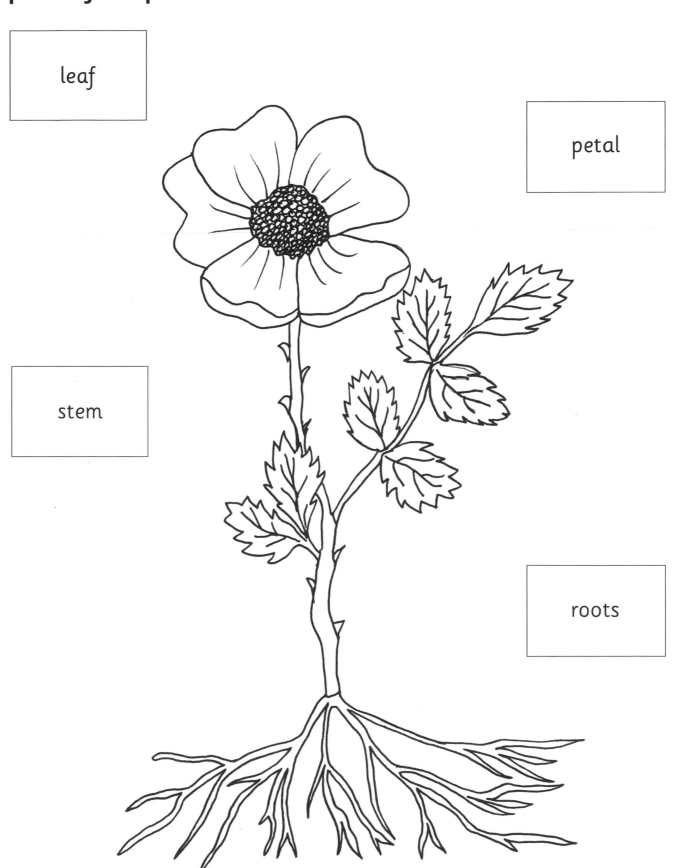

Name: _____ Date: _____

B | Recognize and name parts of plants
 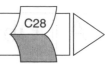

**Colour the petals red, the stem yellow,
the leaves green, the roots brown**

A Observe, describe animals and plants

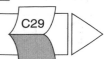

Think of the colour these animals can be, then colour them in carefully

horse

blackbird

cat

worm

snake

rabbit

dog

polar bear

Which animals are always the same colour? _____

_____

_____

B | Observe, describe animals and plants

C30

Think of the colour these plants are and then colour them in carefully

daffodil

rose

cress

cabbage

lettuce

daisy

Put the correct coloured circle around each plant

Blue circle – large leaf

Red circle – small leaf

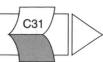
| A | Recognize and name animals | C31 |

Draw a line from each animal to its correct name

mouse

robin

butterfly

sheep

fly

goldfish

Colour them so they look more real

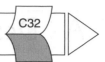
AT2 Level 1

B | Recognize and name animals

C32

Draw a line from each animal to its correct name

blackbird

woodlouse

pig

cow

guinea pig

chicken

Colour them so they look more real

A | Describe basic plant conditions

C33

Take two sets of cress plants

Water one set   Stop watering the other

What do you think will happen to the watered cress? Why?

What do you think will happen to the unwatered cress? Why?

Measure how much each set of cress grows every day

My predictions were right/wrong, because . . .

_____

_____

_____

I have learnt that . . .

_____

_____

_____

Name: _____ Date: _____

B | Describe basic plant conditions

Take two sets of cress plants

Put one set in a warm, well-lit place and water it

> What do you think will happen to the set kept in the light? Why?
>
> _____
>
> _____
>
> _____
>
> _____
>
> _____
>
> _____

Put the other in a warm, dark place and water it

> What do you think will happen to the set kept in the dark? Why?
>
> _____
>
> _____
>
> _____
>
> _____
>
> _____
>
> _____
>
> _____

Measure how much each set grows every day

Draw pictures of each set after a week

This is what happened . . .

_____

_____

I was right/wrong because . . .

_____

A | Reproduction

Link the adult to the young it produces by drawing a line

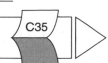

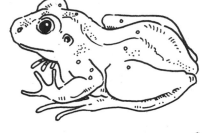

frog

calf

cat

lamb

hen

kitten

sheep

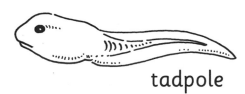

tadpole

chick

cow

Name: _____ Date: _____

B | Reproduction

**Link the adult to the young it produces
by drawing a line**

house martin
chicks in nest

horse

ducklings

goat

foal

duck

kid

house martin

lion

zebra foal

zebra

lion cub

| A | Group using simple features | C37 |

This many children in our class have:

blond hair [   ]   light brown hair [   ]

black hair [   ]   brown hair [   ]

red/ginger hair [   ]

Can you draw a graph to show which is the most common hair colour in our class?

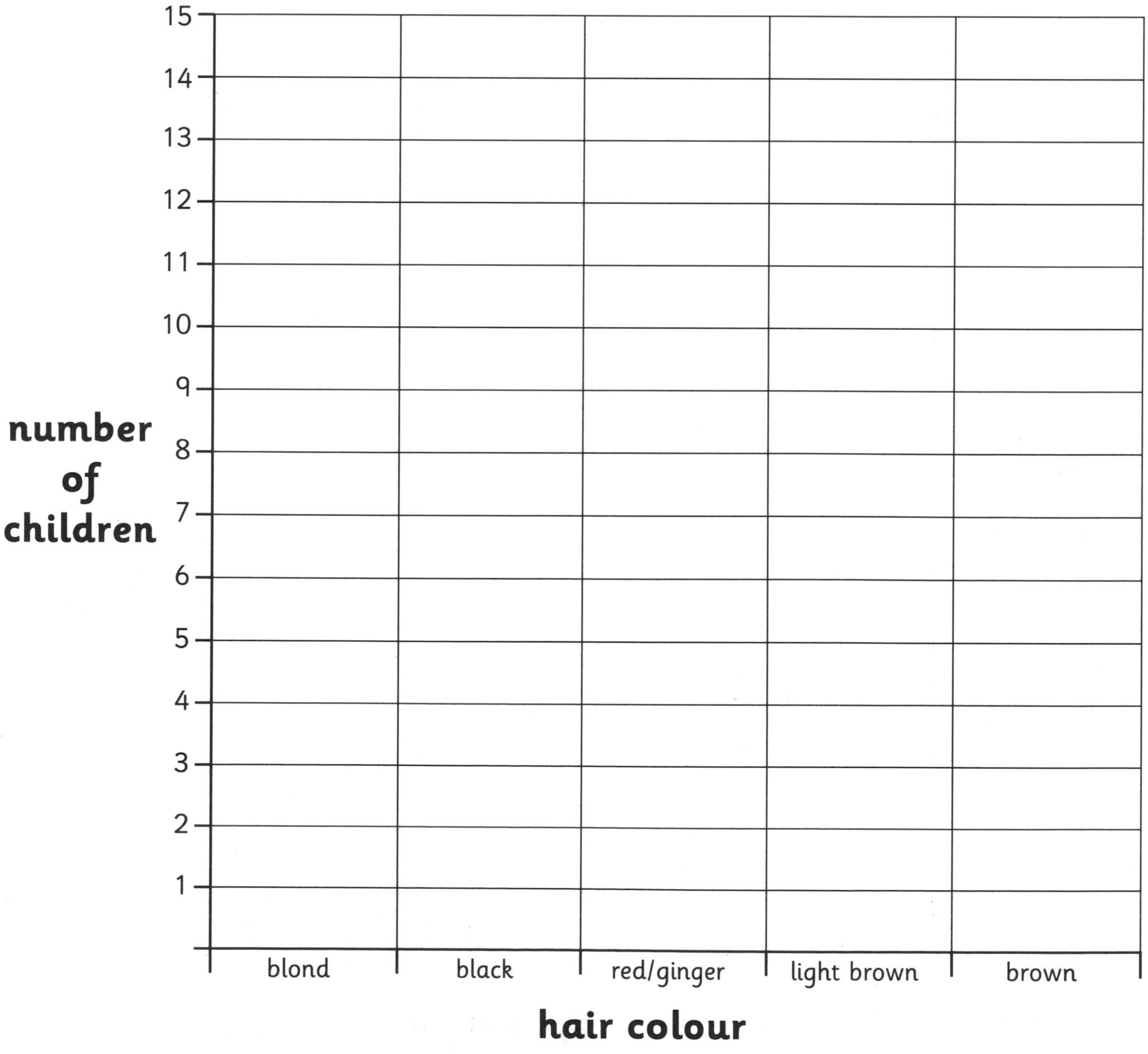

number
of
children

15
14
13
12
11
10
9
8
7
6
5
4
3
2
1

blond   black   red/ginger   light brown   brown

hair colour

B | Group using simple features | C38

This many children in our class have:

blue eyes [ ]   green eyes [ ]

brown eyes [ ]   other colours [ ]

Can you draw a graph to show which is the most common eye colour in our class?

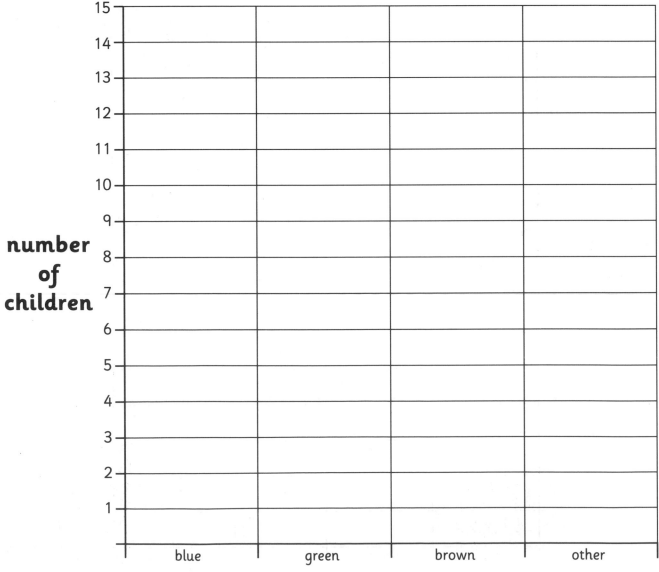

Name: _____ Date: _____

A | Sort according to observable features | C39

Look at the drawings
Draw a red circle round those with six legs
Draw a blue circle round those with eight legs
Draw a yellow circle round those with more than eight legs

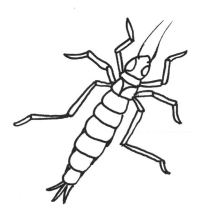

dragonfly larva

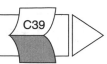

cricket

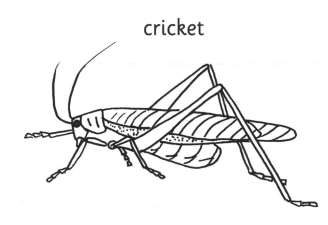

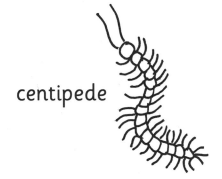

centipede

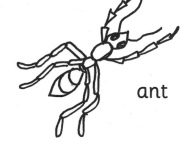

ant

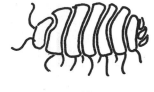

woodlouse

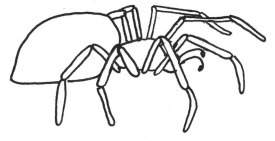

spider

B Sort according to observable features
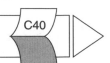

Look at the drawings
Draw a red circle round small leaves
Draw a blue circle round large leaves
Draw a yellow circle round long thin leaves

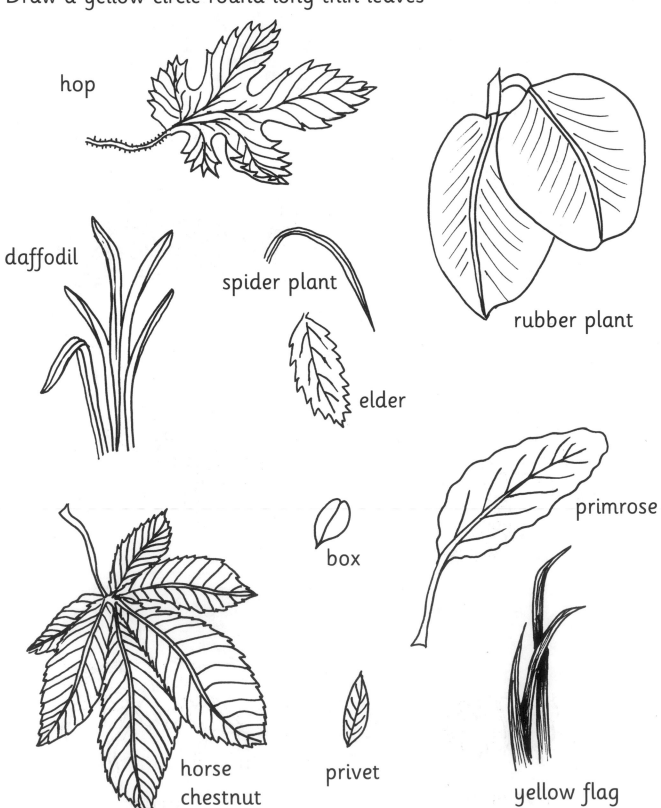

hop

daffodil

spider plant

elder

rubber plant

box

primrose

horse chestnut

privet

yellow flag

| A | Living things in different places | C41 |

Study three different local habitats
Record what you find

Name of local habitat			
How easy is it to find water? Easy/Difficult			
How easy is it to find shade? Easy/Difficult			
Plants found there			
Large animals seen (eg birds)			
Small creature seen (under stone, soil, water, leaves . . .)			

What have you learnt about where plants and animals live?

_____

_____

_____

_____

Name: _____ Date: _____

B | Living things in different places

Draw these living things in the habitats you are most likely to find them

pond

open school field

wood

Name: _____ Date: _____

A | Living and non-living things

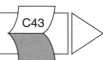

C43

Colour blue everything that all living things do
Leave the others uncoloured

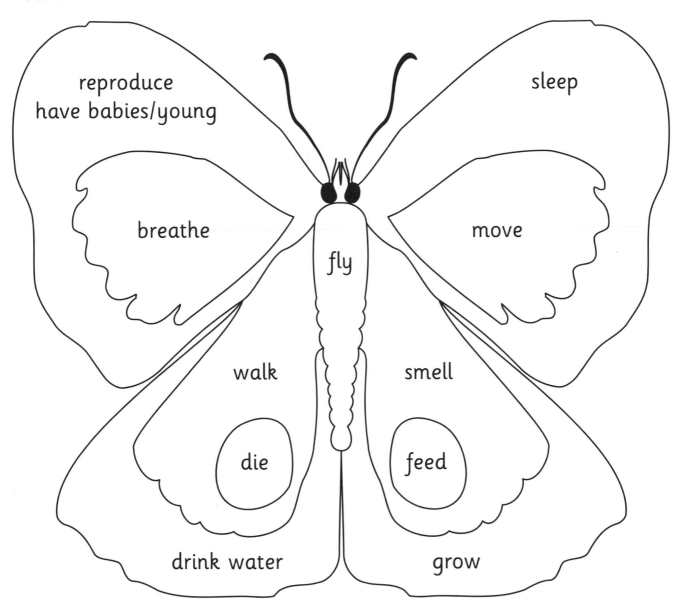

What did you leave out? _____

_____

Why did you leave these out? _____

_____

_____

_____

Name: _____ Date: _____

B │ Living and non-living things

Link the living things to the words which describe what they can do

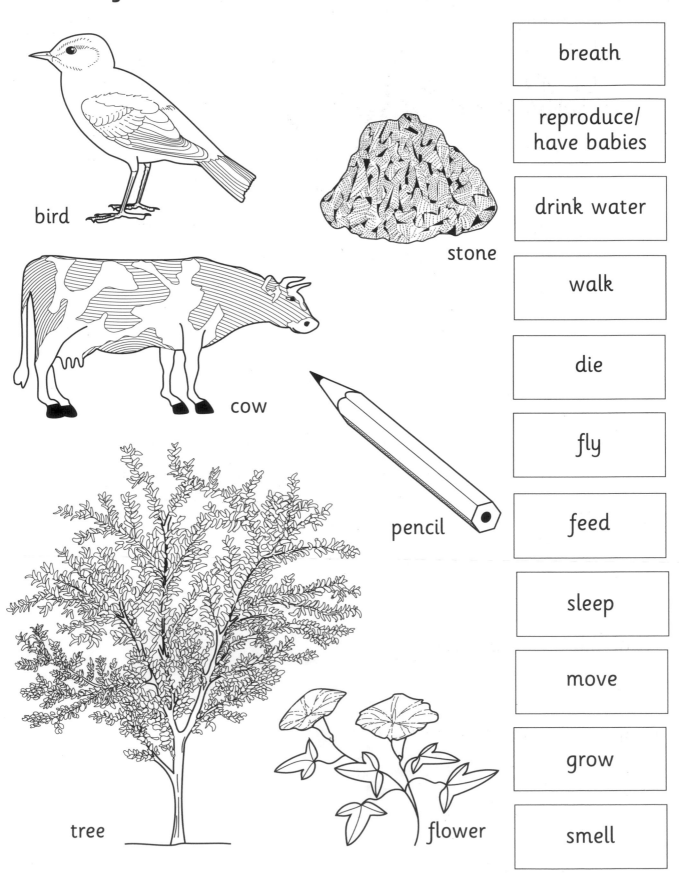

bird

stone

cow

pencil

tree

flower

breath

reproduce/ have babies

drink water

walk

die

fly

feed

sleep

move

grow

smell

Name: _____ Date: _____

| A | Diet affects the health of humans |

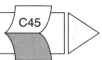

Can you name the four main food groups?

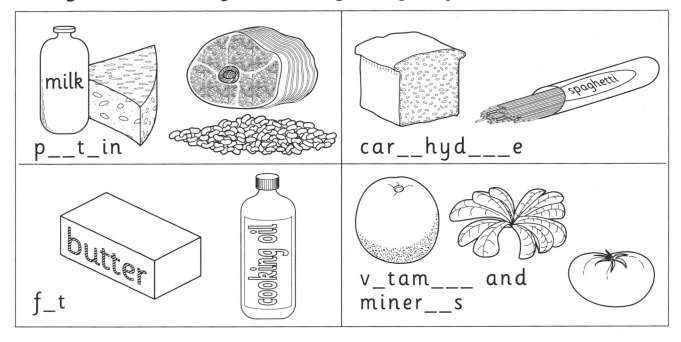

p _ _ t _ in

car _ _ hyd _ _ _ e

f_t

v_tam _ _ _ and miner _ _ s

Which foods should we not eat too much of? Why?

_____

_____

_____

Plan your daily menu (breakfast, lunch and dinner)
Include foods you like and foods from the four main food groups

breakfast	lunch	dinner

Name: _____ Date: _____

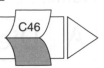

B | **Diet affects the health of humans**

Draw a red circle round foods that give us energy
Draw a blue circle round foods that are body building
Draw a green circle round foods that are full of vitamins
Draw a yellow circle round foods that help to clean out the body

doughnut

sugar

1 kg finest sugar

grapes

sausages

Bran Flakes

crisps

oranges

ham

apples

eggs

brown bread

white bread

Name: _____ Date: _____

A │ Diet affects teeth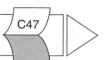

Colour blue the things that are good for your teeth
Colour yellow the things that are bad for your teeth

Look in a mirror
Draw a picture of your teeth (include fillings!)

Why does sugar damage teeth? _____

_____

_____

| B | Diet affects teeth | C48 |

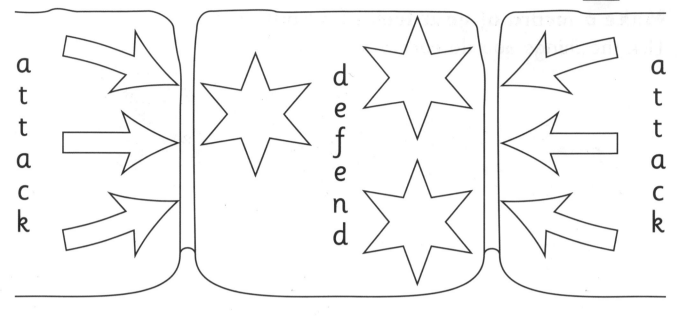

Sort out the attackers and defenders

	defend	attack
sticky sweets		
soft drinks		
apples		
milk		
clean teeth		
iced buns		
hot sugary drinks		
cola (normal)		
toffee		

What do attacking foods have in common? _____

_____

_____

_____

_____

A | Exercise affects the health of humans

C49

Make a record of your leisure activities
Tick the things you do each day

	running	watching TV	swimming	playing football	playing tennis	biking	walking a dog	skipping/jumping	using computers	playing indoors	playing outdoors	lounging/snacking	other
Monday													
Tuesday													
Wednesday													
Thursday													
Friday													
Saturday													
Sunday													

Do you think you take enough exercise to keep fit? _____

_____

_____

_____

How could you improve your fitness? _____

_____

_____

_____

Are you: fit ☐   quite fit ☐   not fit ☐
Tick your choice

Why do you think it's good to be fit? _____

_____

_____

Name: _____   Date: _____

B | Exercise affects the health of humans | C50

Draw a red circle round sedentary activities and a blue circle round activities that provide exercise

using computers

playing outdoors

biking

skipping/jumping

lounging/snacking

walking a dog

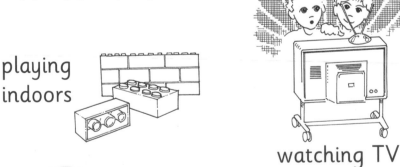
playing indoors

watching TV

swimming

playing tennis

running

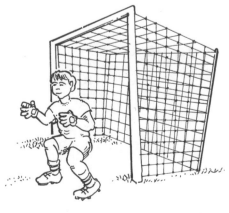
playing football

Name: _____ Date: _____

A | Effect of water and light on plants

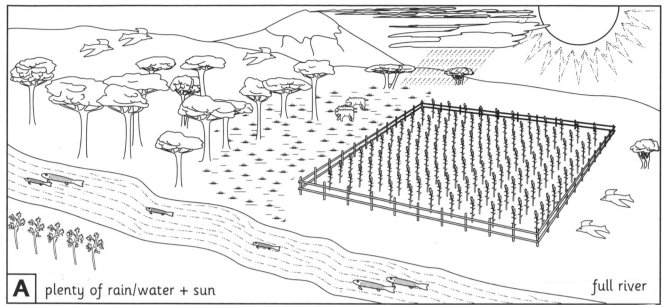

A | plenty of rain/water + sun   full river

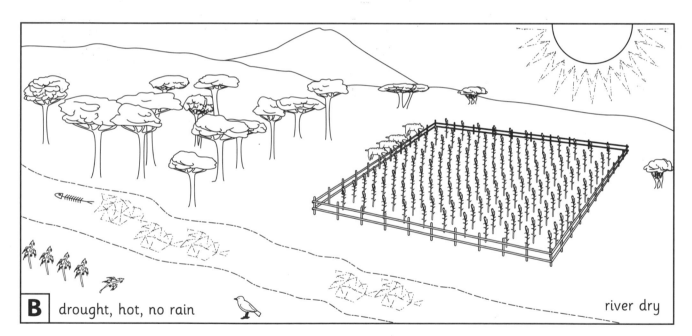

B | drought, hot, no rain   river dry

Describe what you think will happen in the two pictures

A _____

_____

_____

B _____

_____

_____

Name: _____ Date: _____

B | Effect of water and light on plants

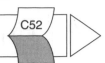

Two identical
healthy green plants
are placed in different positions

1 In sunlight

2 In a dark cupboard

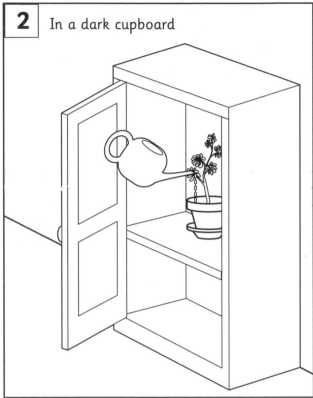

Both are watered properly and kept warm

Will both grow healthily   **yes** ☐   **no** ☐

Tick your answer

Explain your answer _____

_____

_____

_____

_____

| A | Exploring habitats | C53 |

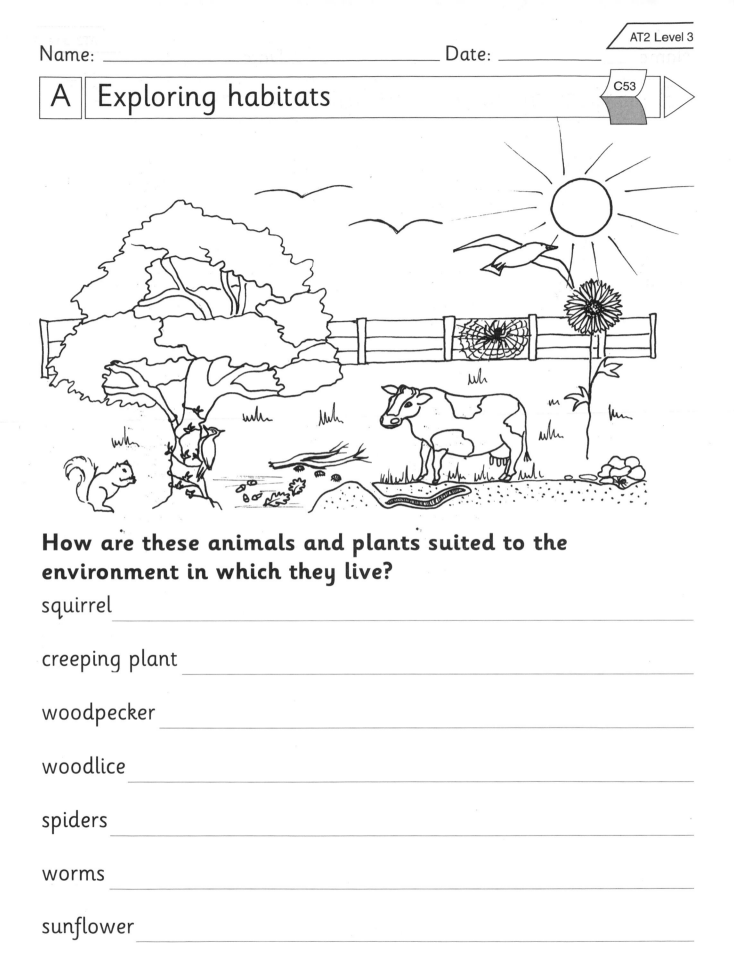

How are these animals and plants suited to the environment in which they live?

squirrel _____

creeping plant _____

woodpecker _____

woodlice _____

spiders _____

worms _____

sunflower _____

birds _____

cow _____

Name: _____ Date: _____

| B | Exploring habitats | C54 |

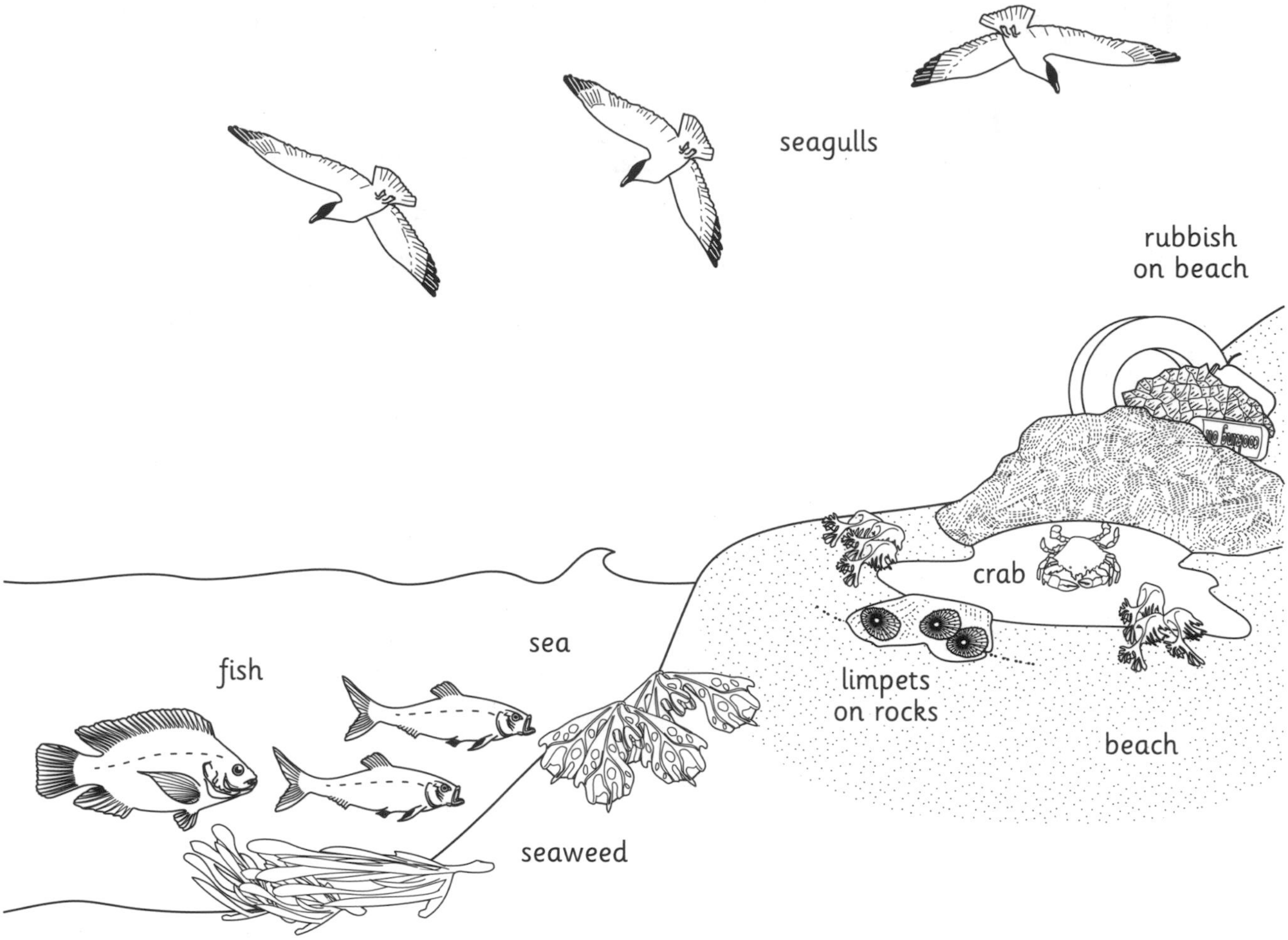

seagulls

rubbish on beach

crab

limpets on rocks

beach

sea

fish

seaweed

How are these animals and plants suited to the environment in which they live?

fish _____

_____

crab _____

_____

seaweed _____

_____

limpets _____

_____

Name: _____ Date: _____

| A | Describe materials | C55 |

Match the materials to their descriptions by using arrows

material	description
wool	slippery, smooth, shiny
wood	brittle, hard, tacky, sticky, shiny
toffee	spongy, soft, springy, hairy
silk	rigid, hard, knobbly, bumpy

Can you think of some more words to describe the materials?

wool		wood	
toffee		silk	

Name: _____ Date: _____

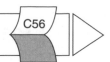

B | Describe materials

Link the materials to their descriptions by using arrows

material	description
metal	bumpy, hard, rigid
plastic	soft, smooth, flexible, stretchy
stone	hard, sharp, smooth
rubber	flexible, smooth, transparent

Can you think of some more words to describe the materials?

metal	stone
plastic	rubber

Name: _____ Date: _____

A | Describe materials by their properties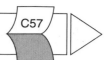

Link each material to its property with an arrow

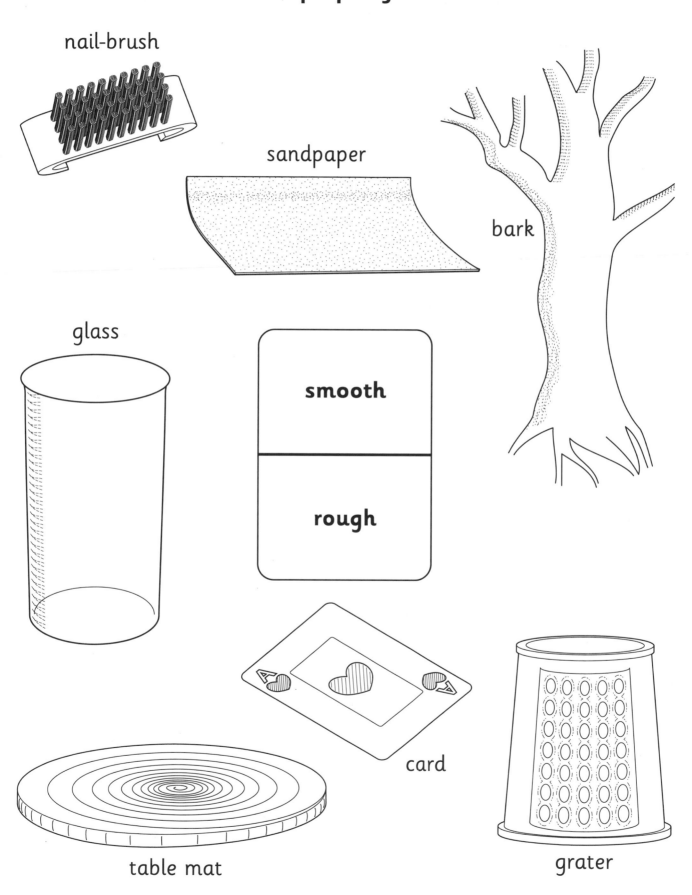

nail-brush

sandpaper

bark

glass

smooth

rough

card

table mat

grater

Name: _____ Date: _____

B | Describe materials by their properties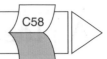

Link each material to its property with an arrow

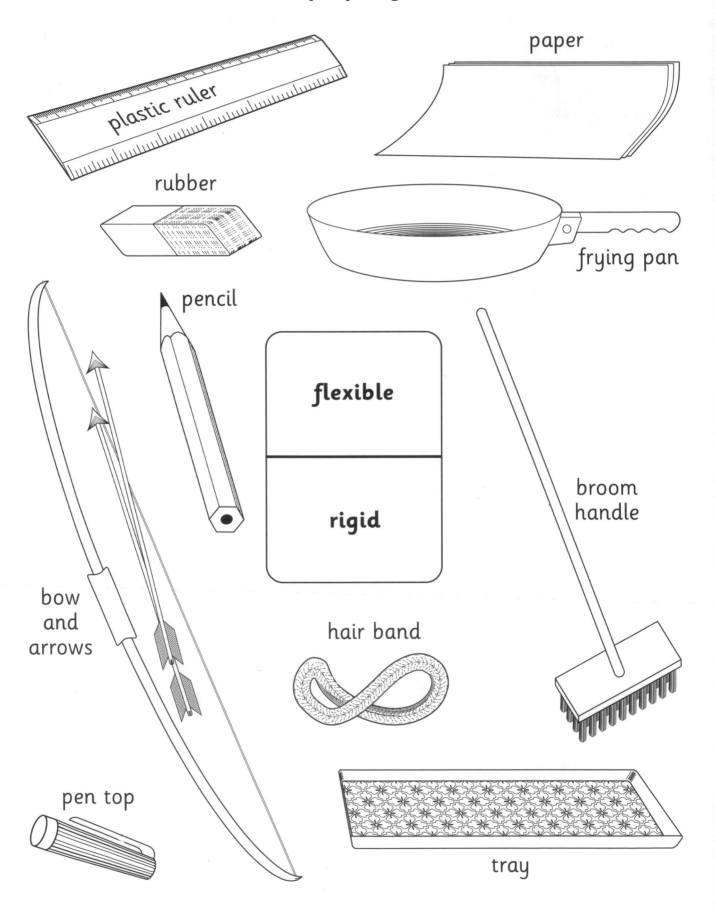

paper

plastic ruler

rubber

frying pan

pencil

flexible

rigid

broom handle

bow and arrows

hair band

pen top

tray

A | Identify materials by their properties

C59

Tick the boxes that describes each material's properties
(may be more than one for each material)

properties	materials									
	balsa	tissue paper	copper tube	coal	pebble	rubber band				
hard										
soft										
rough										
smooth										
dull										
shiny										
heavy										
light										
rigid										
flexible										
bouncy										
waterproof										
absorbent										
transparent										
stretchy										
tears										
opaque										

When you finish the ones listed, add four more of your own

Name: _____ Date: _____

B ‖ Identify materials by their properties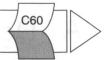

Tick the boxes that describe each material's properties
(may be more than one for each material)

properties	materials									
	tracing paper	corru-gated plastic	clear glass	earthen-ware	alumin-ium foil	con-crete				
hard										
soft										
rough										
smooth										
dull										
shiny										
heavy										
light										
rigid										
flexible										
bouncy										
waterproof										
absorbent										
transparent										
stretchy										
tears										
opaque										

When you finish the ones listed, add four more of your own

Name: _____ Date: _____

| A | Describe similarities and differences | |

differences	similarities	differences
	cotton wool	
	silk rubber	
	aluminium copper	
	brick wood	
	coal chalk	
	water custard	

B	Describe similarities and differences	C62

differences	similarities	differences
	sand sugar	
	paper card	
	custard jelly	
	wood coal	
	water lemonade	
	fur wool	

A | Sorting materials

Walk around the inside of the school, look at the materials
it is made from
Draw a picture of parts of the school, note materials and
simple properties as in the example

Parts of school I have seen	Picture and name materials	properties of materials
Example: windows	wood — glass	wood – hard, rigid glass – transparent, hard

Can you sort the materials into groups? _____

_____

How have you sorted them? _____

_____

Name: _____ Date: _____

B │ Sorting materials

Walk around the outside of the school, look at the materials
it is made from
Draw a picture of parts of the school, note materials and
simple properties as in the example

Parts of school I have seen	Picture and name materials	Properties of materials
Example: drainpipe	plastic	plastic – hard, rigid

Can you sort the materials into groups? _____

_____

_____

How have you sorted them? _____

_____

_____

A | Changes in materials

C65

Write or draw pictures to show the effect of heating and cooling
on these materials

Material	Effect of heating	Effect of cooling
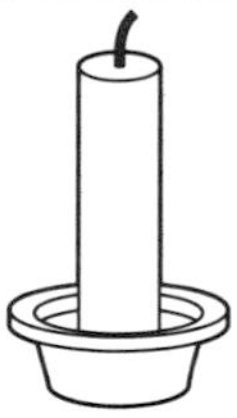 candle		
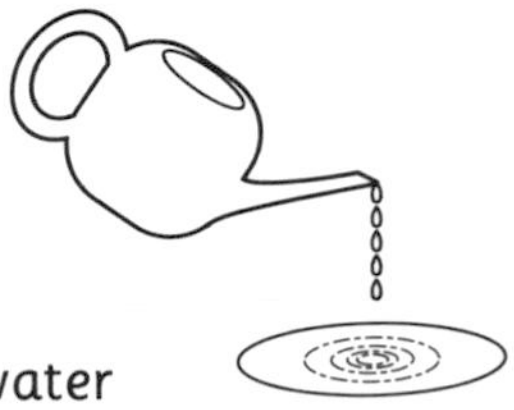 water		
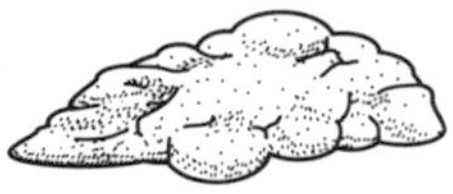 Back Ton oven clay		
 jelly		
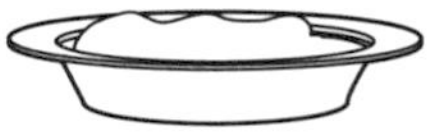 custard		
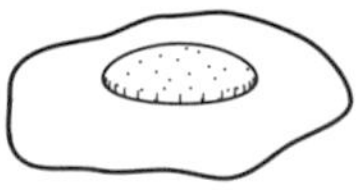 raw egg		

What did you see? _____

_____

_____

_____

Name: _____ Date: _____

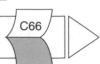

| B | Changes in materials |

C66

Write or draw pictures to show the effect of stretching and bending on these materials

Material	Effect of stretching	Effect of bending
Plasticine		
soap		
dough		
toffee		
wool		
rubber		

What did you see? _____

_____

_____

_____

A Sorting materials by their properties C67

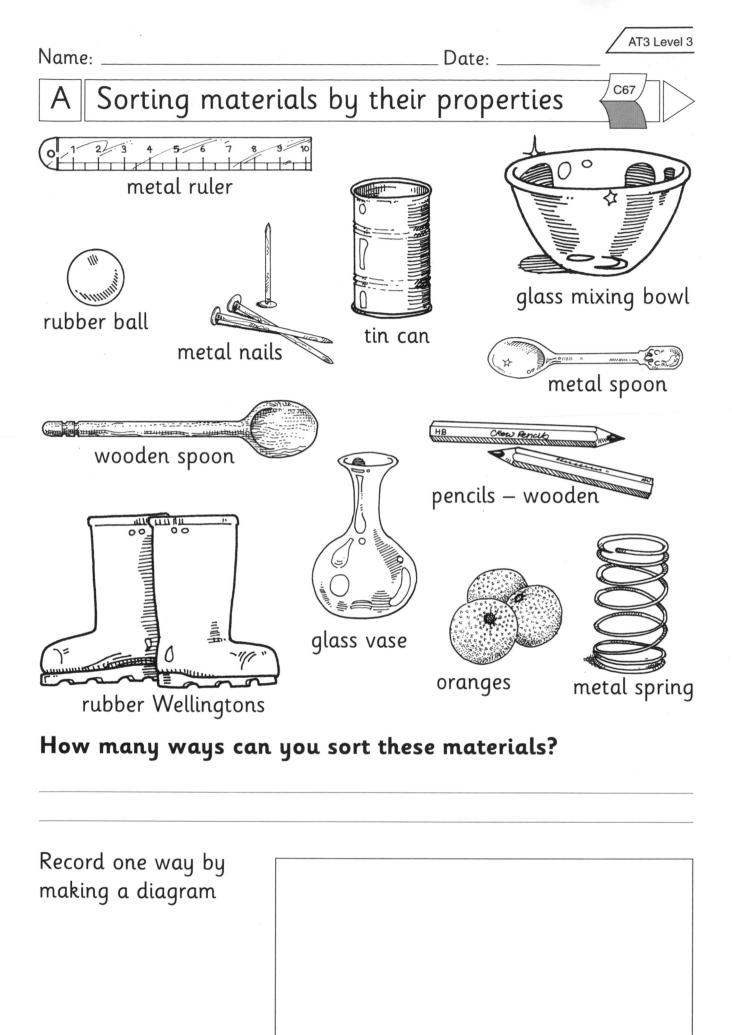

metal ruler

rubber ball

metal nails

tin can

glass mixing bowl

metal spoon

wooden spoon

pencils – wooden

rubber Wellingtons

glass vase

oranges

metal spring

How many ways can you sort these materials?

_____

_____

Record one way by
making a diagram

Name: _____ Date: _____

| B | Sorting materials by their properties | C68 |

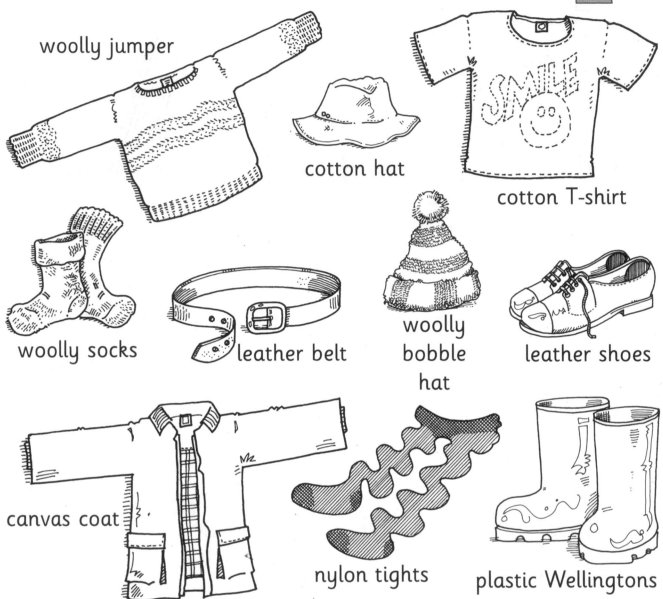

woolly jumper

cotton hat

cotton T-shirt

woolly socks

leather belt

woolly bobble hat

leather shoes

canvas coat

nylon tights

plastic Wellingtons

How many ways can you sort these materials?

_____

Record one way by making a diagram

Name: _____ Date: _____

| A | Suitable materials |

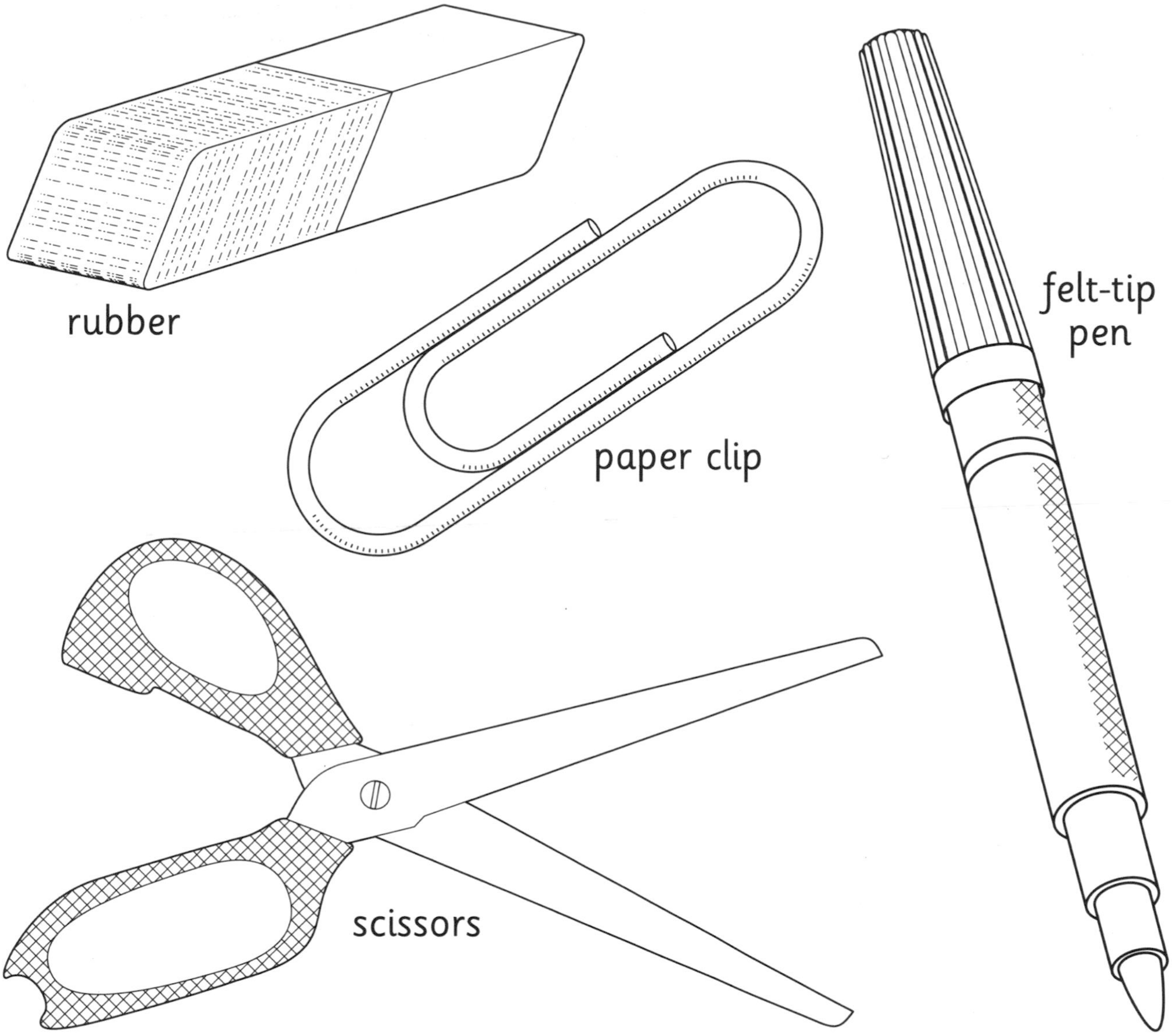

C69

rubber

paper clip

felt-tip pen

scissors

Which of these can conduct electricity? _____

_____

_____

Test them. Were you right? _____

_____

_____

Why is wire used in electrical circuits? _____

_____

_____

B Suitable materials

orange

plastic spoon

metal spoon

6-inch nail

Which of these can conduct electricity? _____

_____

_____

Test them. Were you right? _____

_____

_____

What kind of material is best for making electrical circuits?

_____

Why? _____

_____

A ‖ Reversible/irreversible changes

Record the temperatures

state of water	temperature (°C)
tap water	
freezing water	
frozen water (ice)	
melting ice: 1 _____ 2 _____ 3 _____	
boiling water	

Can you fill in the gaps?

Tap water is_____ to make ice

Ice is_____ to make water

Water is_____ to make steam

Steam is_____ to make water

B | Reversible/irreversible changes

Observe and make drawing of the eggs

state of egg	observational drawing of egg, and notes
raw egg	_____ _____ _____
boiled egg – one minute	_____ _____ _____
boiled egg – three minutes	_____ _____ _____
boiled egg – seven minutes	_____ _____ _____

What happens to the egg as it cooks? _____

_____

_____

Can a boiled egg be returned to a raw condition?

yes [ ]   no [ ]

Name: _____ Date: _____

| A | Natural and made materials | 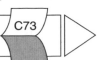 |

Colour natural materials green and made materials red

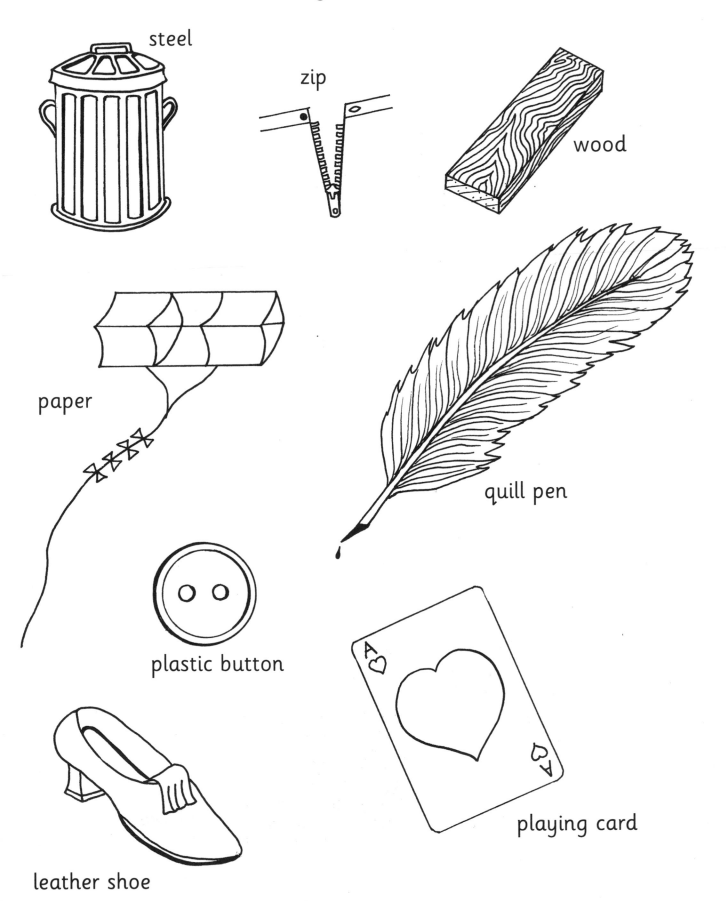

steel

zip

wood

paper

quill pen

plastic button

playing card

leather shoe

B Natural and made materials

C74

Colour natural materials green and made materials red

sea shell

light bulb

pencil rubber

comic

telephone

wool

ball point pen

clay pot

radio

hay bale

Name: _____ Date: _____

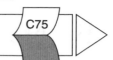

A | Mass and size of materials

Use all of each piece to make the models

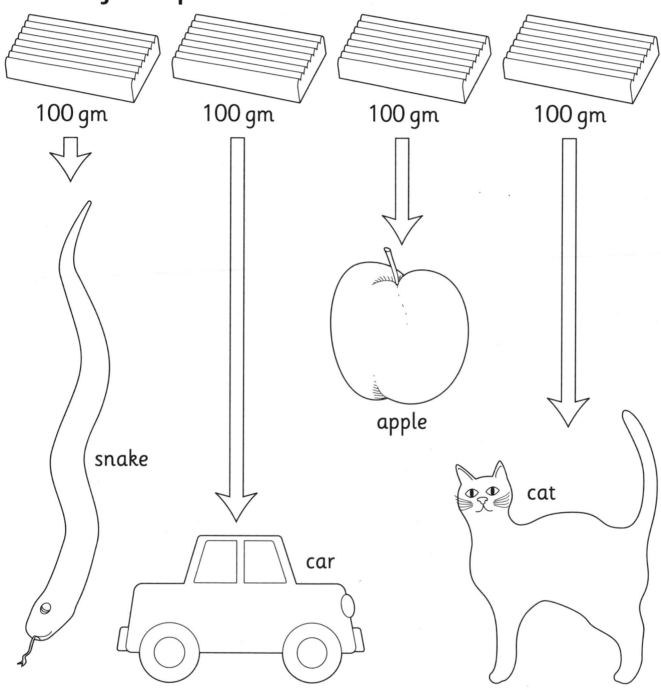

100 gm   100 gm   100 gm   100 gm

snake

apple

car

cat

Will all the models weigh the same?

yes [ ]   no [ ]

Explain your answer _____

_____

_____

B | Mass and size of materials

C76

Which weighs the most:
six ice cubes or the water formed when they melt?

ice   **or**   **water**

Tick ✓ your choice: Ice cubes weigh most ☐

Water weighs most ☐

Ice and water weigh the same ☐

Explain your choice _____

_____

_____

_____

_____

A ▌ Describe changes in light

C77

What changes in light happen?
Colour the bulb if it will light up

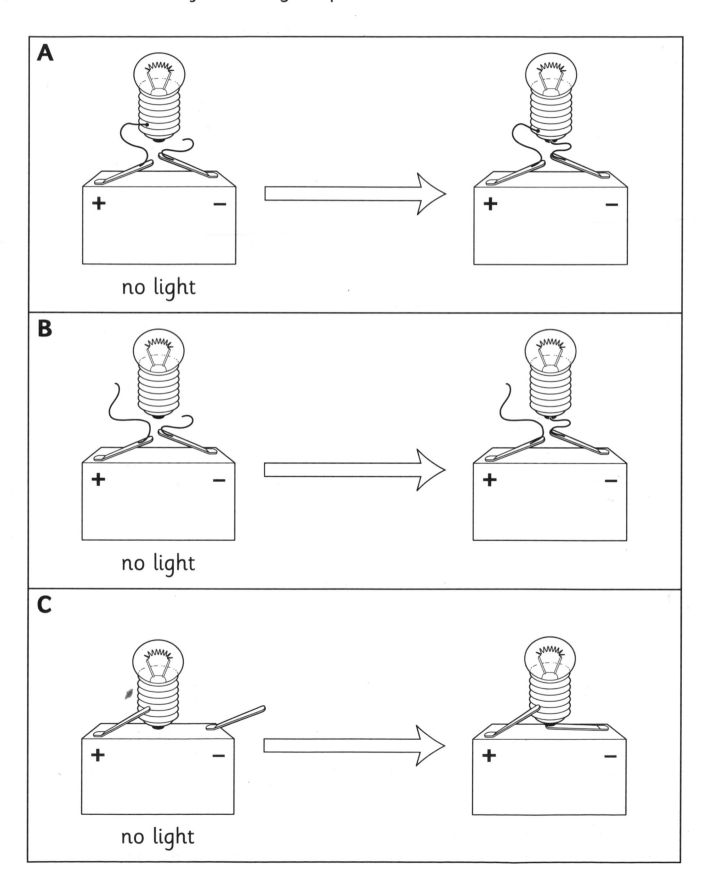

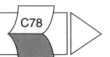
B | Describe changes in light

What changes in light happen?
Colour the bulb if it will light up

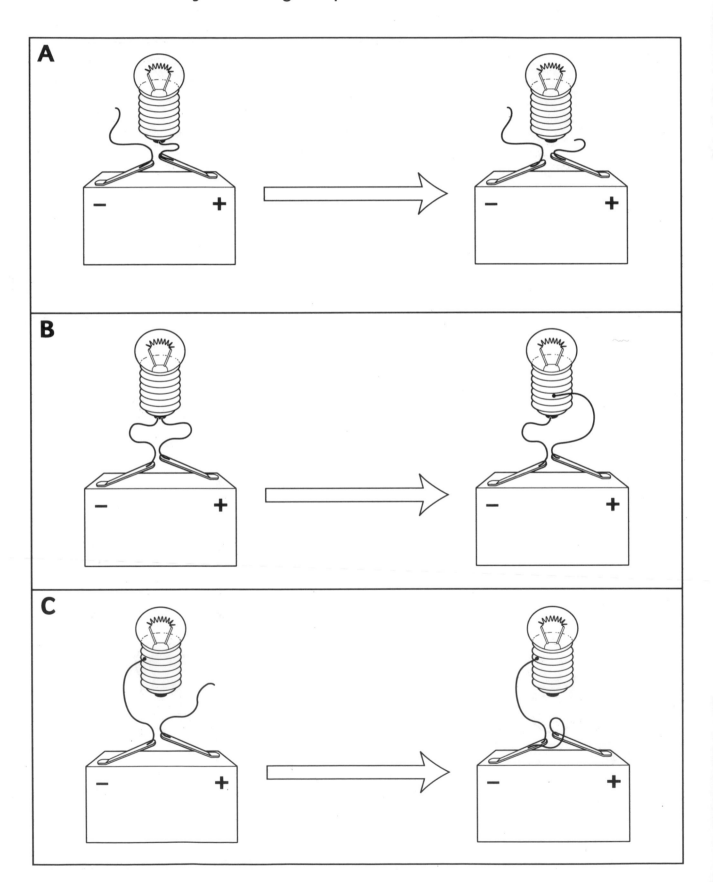

Name: _____ Date: _____

A Describe changes in sound

Colour blue the objects that make a loud sound
Colour red the objects that make a soft sound

lion roaring

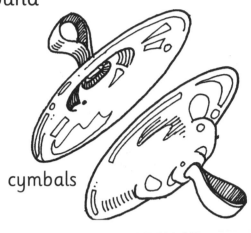

cymbals

feather falling to ground

grandfather clock

leaf falling to ground

motorbike

town crier with bell

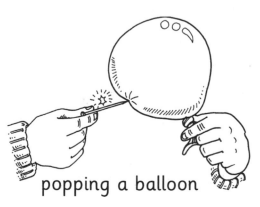

popping a balloon

Name: _____ Date: _____

B Describe changes in sound

C80

Colour blue the objects that make with a loud sound
Colour red the objects that make a soft sound

someone shouting
in the playground

someone whispering

jet plane

someone asleep
(not snoring!)

firework

snake slithering

someone tiptoeing
past a sleeping baby

banging
a bass drum

Name: _____ Date: _____

A Pushing and pulling objects

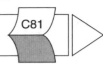

Talk about the pushes and pulling in the pictures

Child's comments:

Child's comments:

Child's comments:

Child's comments:

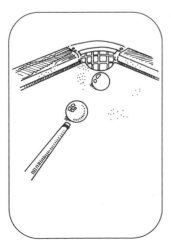

Child's comments:

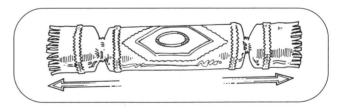

Child's comments:

Name: _____   Date: _____

B Pushing and pulling objects

Talk about the pushes and pulling in the pictures

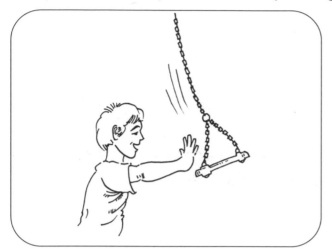

Child's comments:

Child's comments:

Child's comments:

Child's comments:

Child's comments:

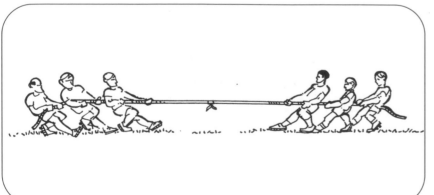

Name: _____ Date: _____

A Identify and name light sources

C83

Draw circles round the places where light comes from

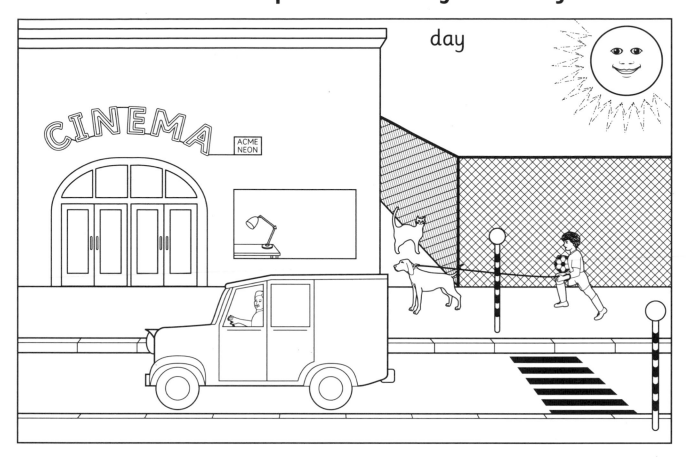

Draw two more things that light comes from in the daytime

Can you name them?

_____   _____

_____   _____

Name: _____ Date: _____

| B | Identify and name light sources |
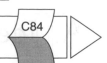

Draw circles round the places where light comes from

night

ALL NIGHT SHOP

ACME NEON

Draw two more things that light comes from at night time

Can you name them?

_____ _____

Name: _____ Date: _____

A | Identify and name sound sources

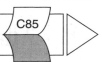

C85

Draw circles round the places where sound comes from

Draw two more things that sound comes from at night time

Can you name them?

_____   _____

_____   _____

Name: _____ Date: _____

B | Identify and name sound sources

Draw circles around the places where sound comes from

Draw two more things that sound comes from in the daytime

Can you name them?

_____   _____

_____   _____

Name: _____ Date: _____

| A | How bulbs work |

Colour the bulb if it will light up

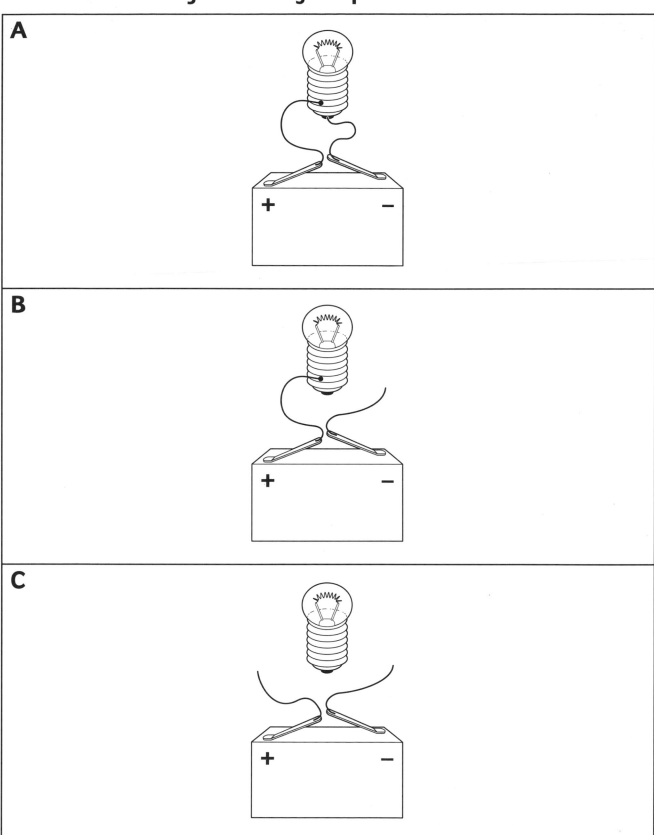

A

B

C

B | How bulbs work

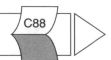

Colour the bulb if it will light up

A

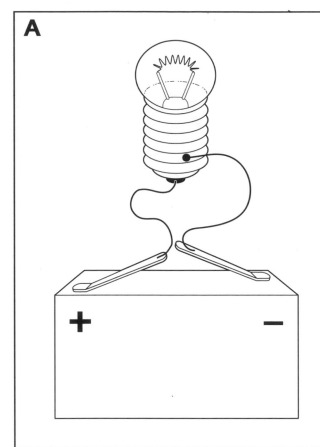

B

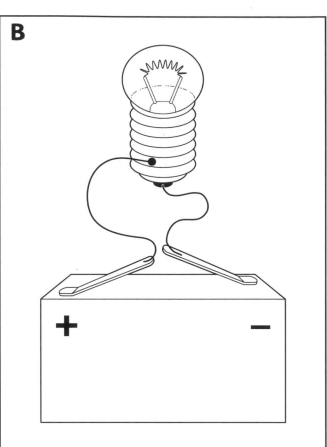

C

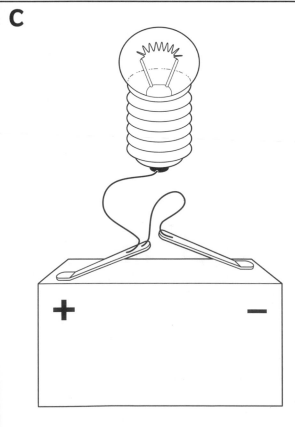

D

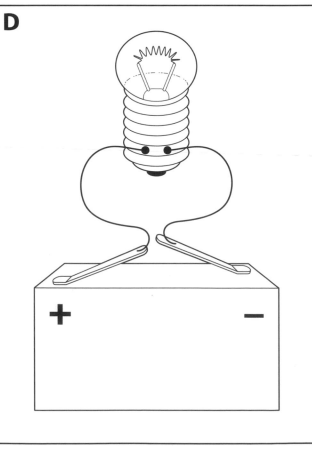

Colour the bulb if it will light up

Name: _____ Date: _____

A | Sounds

Link the words to the correct instruments

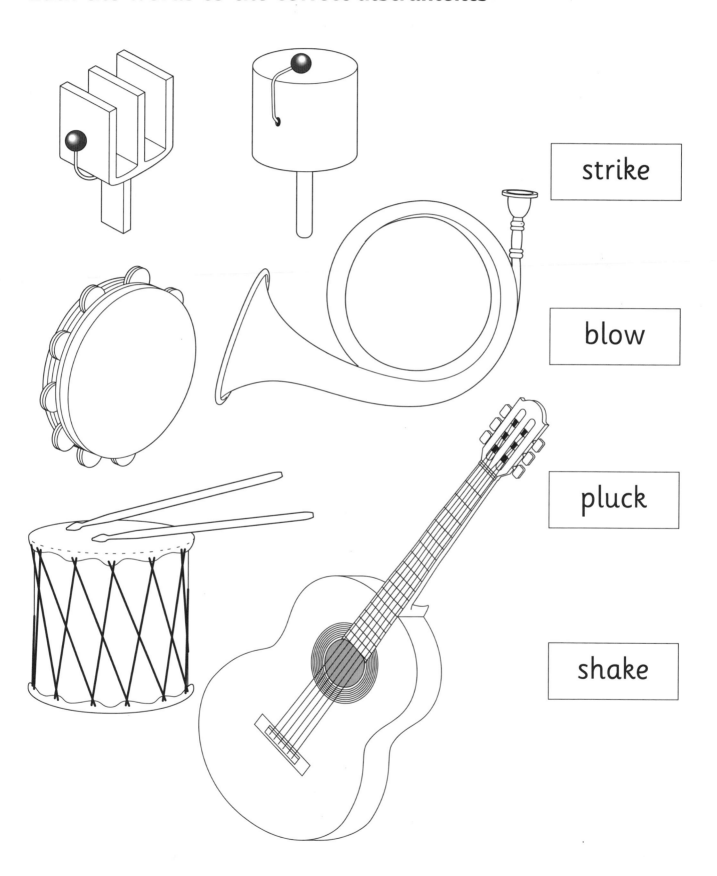

strike

blow

pluck

shake

Name: _____ Date: _____

B │ Sounds

C90

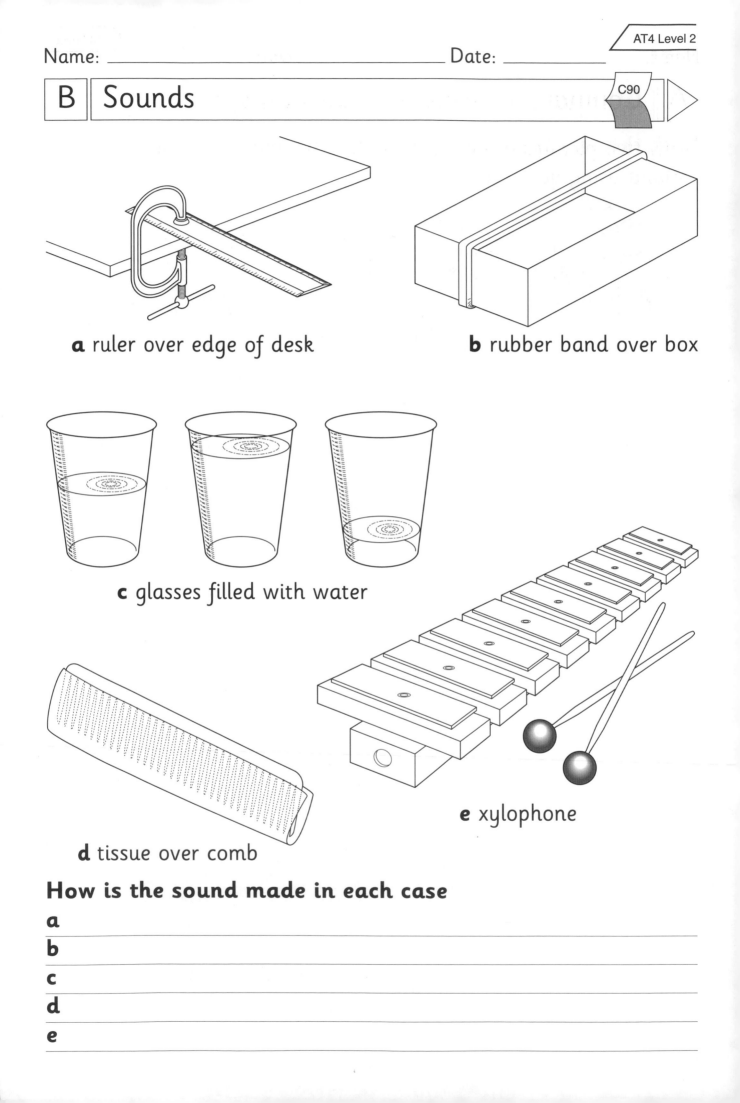

a ruler over edge of desk

b rubber band over box

c glasses filled with water

d tissue over comb

e xylophone

How is the sound made in each case

a _____

b _____

c _____

d _____

e _____

Name: _____ Date: _____

AT4 Level 2

A | **Compare movement – direction/speed** C91

Draw two pictures of how you can start a toy car moving without using your hands

Draw two pictures of how you can stop a toy car from moving without using your hands

Does a car travel further if you push it hard?

yes [ ]   no [ ]

How can you make the toy car travel further? _____

_____

Name: _____ Date: _____

B | Compare movement – direction/speed   C92

Draw two pictures of how you can start a ball moving without using your hands

Draw two pictures of how you can stop a ball from moving without using your hands

Does a ball travel further if you push it hard?

yes [ ]   no [ ]

How can you make the ball travel further? _____

_____

_____

Name: _____ Date: _____

A | Light fails because of break in circuit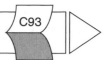

C93

Predict what will happen
Record result of testing the circuits

circuit	prediction	test result
A		
B		
C		
D		
E		

B Light fails because of break in circuit

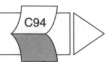

C94

Predict what will happen
Record result of testing the circuits

circuit	prediction	test result
A		
B		
C		
D		

Name: _____ Date: _____

A | Applied forces affect direction/speed

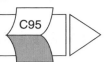

Draw arrows to show what will happen to the objects
in the pictures below

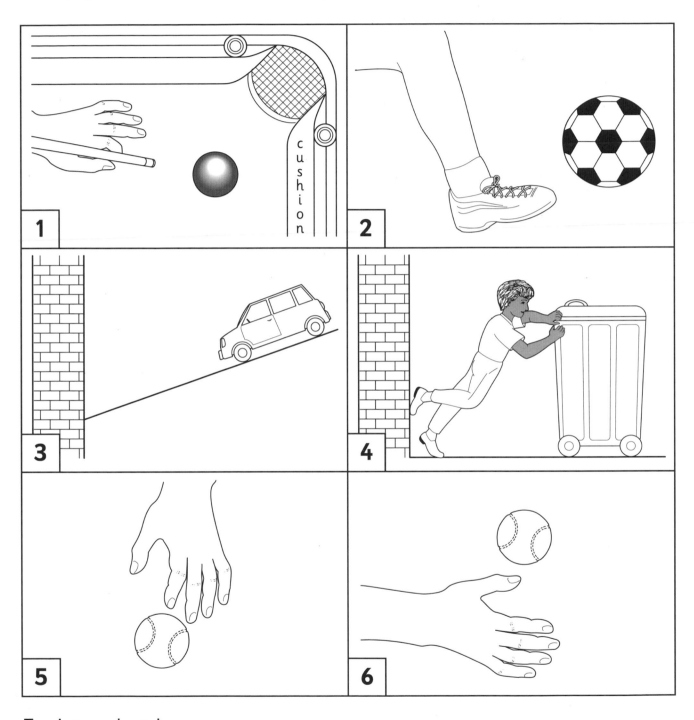

Explain what happens _____

_____

_____

_____

Name: _____ Date: _____

B | Applied forces affect direction/speed

Draw arrows to show what will happen to the objects
in the pictures below

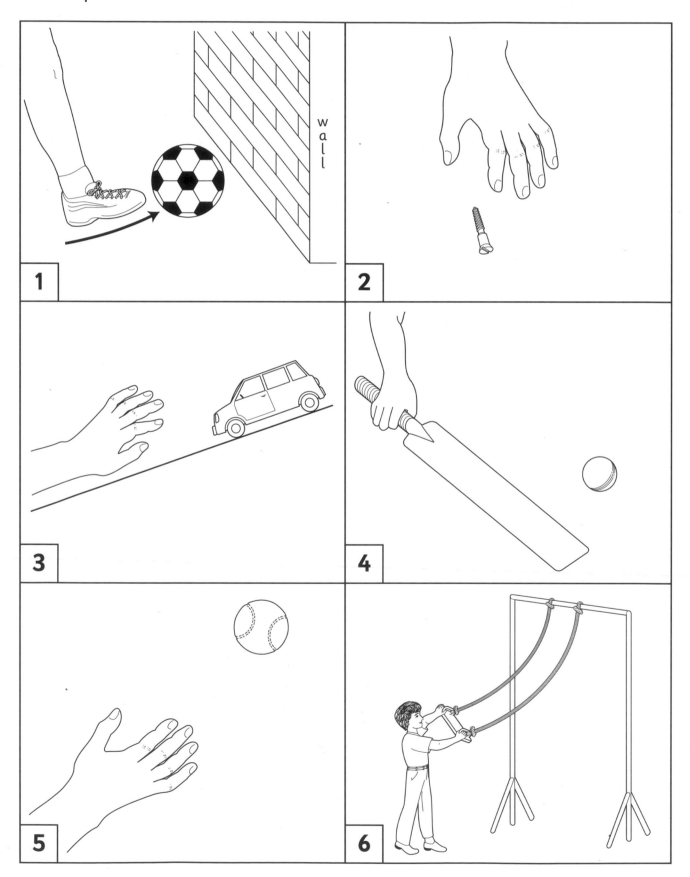

Name: _____ Date: _____

A | Sideways pushes/pulls cause swerves

ball hits shoulder

What do you think might happen after the ball glances off the defender's shoulder? _____

_____

Why? _____

_____

Name: _____ Date: _____

| B | Sideways pushes/pulls cause swerves | |

parked car

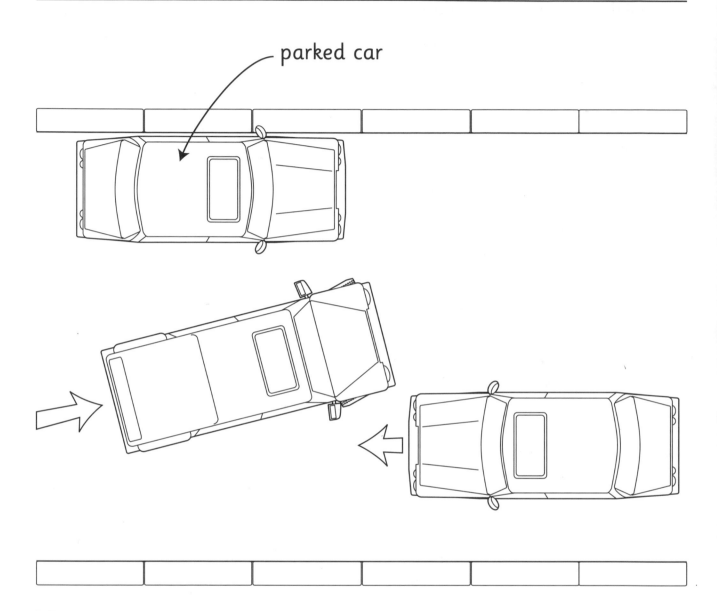

The two moving cars cannot stop. What do you think will happen?

_____

_____

Why? _____

_____

_____

Name: _____ Date: _____

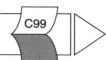

A Pulls/pushes can change some shapes

C99

Make drawings of what you think will happen
Use arrows to show the direction of forces

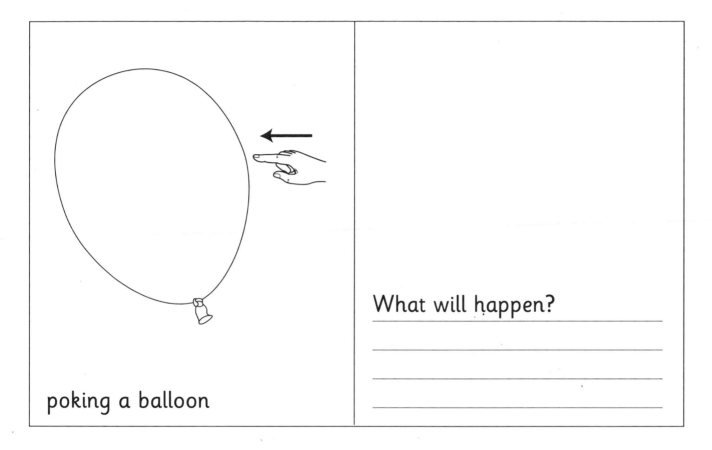

poking a balloon

What will happen?
_____
_____
_____
_____

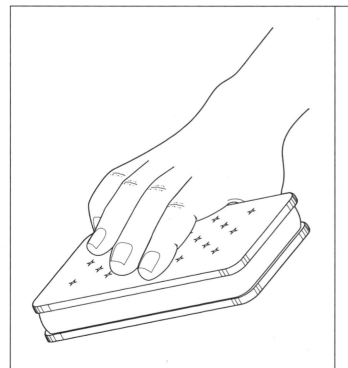

squeezing an ice cream wafer

What will happen? _____
_____
_____
_____
_____

B Pulls/pushes can change some shapes

Make drawings of what you think will happen
Use arrows to show the direction of forces

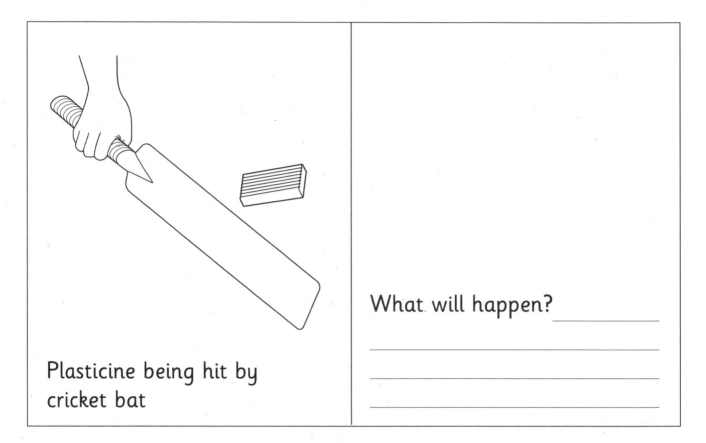

Plasticine being hit by
cricket bat

What will happen? _____

_____

_____

_____

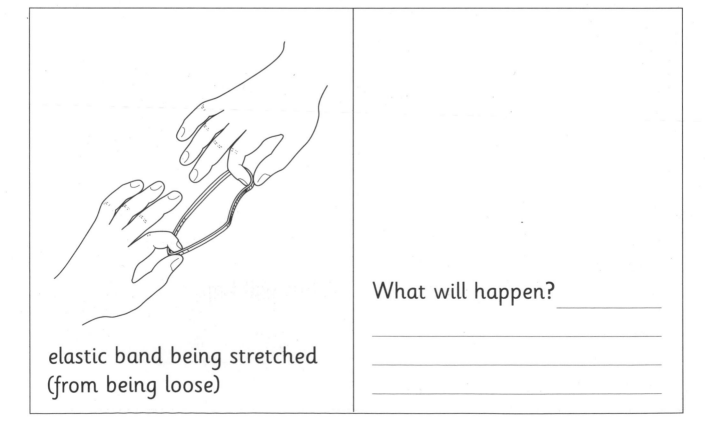

elastic band being stretched
(from being loose)

What will happen? _____

_____

_____

_____

Name: _____ Date: _____

A | Sounds become louder

Circle which ones will sound louder
(you could circle both)

Name: _____ Date: _____

| B | Sounds become louder | C102 |

Circle which ones will sound louder
(you could circle both)

Record Sheet 1 Class Record

Class	Level	Date			
		Teacher's name			

Name	AT1	AT2	AT3	AT4

Record Sheet 2 Child's Record

Name	Date of birth	Teacher's Initials

AT1

Level 1	Date	Level 2	Date	Level 3	Date
1 Features/living things		4 Suggestions/predictions		11 Observe/predict	
2 Features/objects		5 Suggestions/suggestions		12 Fair test	
3 Features/animals		6 Suggestions/conclusions			
		7 Compare living things			
		8 Compare events			
		9 Compare objects			
		10 Predict/record			

AT2

Level 1	Date	Level 2	Date	Level 3	Date
1 Recog/name body parts		5 Plant conditions		10 Living/non-living	
2 Recog/name plant parts		6 Reproduction		11 Diet & health	
3 Observe animals/plants		7 Group by features		12 Diet & teeth	
4 Recog/name animals		8 Sort by features		13 Exercise & health	
		9 Living things/places		14 Light/water & plants	
				15 Habitats	

AT3

Level 1	Date	Level 2	Date	Level 3	Date
1 Describe materials		3 Identify materials		7 Sort by properties	
2 Materials/properties		4 Similarities/differences		8 Suitable materials	
		5 Sorting materials		9 Reversible/irreversible	
		6 Changes in materials		10 Natural/made mats	
				11 Mass/size	

AT4

Level 1	Date	Level 2	Date	Level 3	Date
1 Changes in light		6 How bulbs work		9 Circuits	
2 Changes in sound		7 Sounds		10 Applied forces	
3 Push/pull		8 Direction/speed		11 Sideways push/pull	
4 Light sources				12 Forces on soft objects	
5 Sound sources				13 Sound volume	